A MAINSAIL
HAUL

Other Sailing Classics

A Mainsail
Haul

JOHN MASEFIELD

GRAFTON BOOKS
A Division of the Collins Publishing Group

LONDON GLASGOW
TORONTO SYDNEY AUCKLAND

Grafton Books
A Division of the Collins Publishing Group
8 Grafton Street, London W1X 3LA

First published 1905
Revised and enlarged 1913
Reissued with two new pieces ('Some Famous Wrecks' and 'On
    Moonsails') 1954
This edition published by Grafton Books 1987

British Library Cataloguing in Publication Data

Masefield, John
    A mainsail haul.
    I. Title
    823'.912[F]   PR6025.A77

    ISBN 0–246–13177–2

Printed in Great Britain by
Robert Hartnoll (1985) Ltd, Bodmin, Cornwall

Photoset by Rowland Phototypesetting Ltd
Bury St Edmunds, Suffolk

CONTENTS

DON ALFONSO'S TREASURE HUNT

Now in the old days, before steam, there was a young Spanish buck who lived in Trinidad, and his name was Don Alfonso. Now Trinidad is known, in a way of speaking, among sailormen, as Hell's Lid, or Number One Hatch, by reason of its being very hot there. They've a great place there, which they show to folk, where it's like a cauldron of pitch. It bubbles pitch out of the earth, all black and hot, and you see great slimy workings, all across, like ropes being coiled inside. And talk about smell there! – talk of brimstone! – why, it's like a cattle-ship gone derelict, that's what that place is like.

Now by reason of the heat there, the folk of those parts – a lot of Spaniards mostly, Dagoes and that – they don't do nothing but just sit around. When they turn out of a morning they get some yellow paper and some leaf tobacco, and they rolls what they calls cigarellers and sticks them in their ears like pens. That's their day's work, that is – rolling them yellow cigarellers. Well, then, they set around and they smokes – big men, too, most of them – and they put flowers in their hats – red roses and that – and that's how they pass their time.

Now this Don Alfonso he was a terror, he was; for they've got a licker in those parts. If you put some of it on a piece of paint-work – and this is gospel that I'm giving you – that paint it comes off like you was using turps. Now Don Alfonso he was a terror at that licker – and that's the sort of Dago-boy Alfonso was.

Now Alfonso's mother was a widow, and he was her only child, like in the play.

Now one time, when Don Alfonso was in the pulperia (that's Spanish for grog-shop), he was a-bluin' down that licker the same as you or I would be bluin' beer. And there was a gang of Dagoes there, and all of them chewing the rag, and all of them going for the vino – that's the Spanish name for wine – v-i-n-o. It's red wine, vino is; they give it you in port to save water.

Now among them fancy Dagoes there was a young Eye-talian who'd been treasure-hunting, looking for buried treasure, in that Blue Nose ship which went among the islands. Looking for gold, he'd been, gold that was buried by the pirates. They're a gay crew, them Blue Nose fellers. What'd the pirates bury treasure for? Not them. It stands to reason. Did you ever see a shellback go reeving his dollars down a rabbit-warren? It stands to reason. Golden dollar coins indeed. Bury them customs fellers if you like. Now this young Dago, he was coming it proud about that treasure. In one of them Tortugas, he was saying, or off of the Chagres, or if not there among them smelly Samballs, there's tons of it lying in a foot of sand with a skellinton on the top. They used to kill a nigger, he was saying, when they buried their blunt, so's his ghost would keep away thieves. There's a sight of thieves, ain't there, in them smelly Samballs? An' niggers ain't got no ghosts, not that I ever heard.

Oh, he was getting gay about that buried treasure. Gold there was, and silver dollars and golden jewels, and I don't know what all. 'And I knows the place,' he says, 'where it's all lying,' and out he pulls a chart with a red crost on it, like in them Deadwood Dicky books. And what with the vino and that there licker, he got them Dagoes strung on a line. So the end of it was that Don Alfonso he came down with the blunt. And that gang of Dagoes they charters a

brigantine – she'd a Bible name to her, as is these Dagoes'
way – and off they sails a galley-vaunting looking for gold
with a skellinton on the top. Now one dusk, just as they
was getting out the lamps and going forward with the
kettle, they spies a land ahead and sings out 'Land, O!' By
dark they was within a mile of shore, hove-to off of a
lighthouse that was burning a red flare. Now the old man
he comes to Alfonso, and he says, 'I dunno what land this
may be. There's no land due to us this week by my
account. And that red flare there; there's no light burning
a flare nearer here than Sydney.' 'Let go your anchor,'
says Don Alfonso, 'for land there is, and where there's
land there's rum. And lower away your dinghy, for I'm
going in for a drink. You can take her in, mister, with two
of the hands, and then lay aboard till I whistle.' So they
lower the dinghy, and Don Alfonso takes some cigarellers,
and ashore he goes for that there licker.

Now when he sets foot ashore, and the boat was gone
off, Don Alfonso he walked up the quay in search of a
pulperia. And it was a strange land he was in, and that's
the truth. Quiet it was, and the little white houses still as
corfins, and only a lamp or two burning, and never a
sound nor a song. Oh, a glad lad was Don Alfonso when he
sees a nice little calaboosa lying to leeward, with a red
lamp burning in the stoop. So in he goes for a dram – into
the grog-house, into a little room with a fire lit and a little
red man behind the bar. Now it was a caution was that
there room, for instead of there bein' casks like beer or vino
casks, there was only corfins. And the little red man he
gives a grin, and he gives the glad hand to Don Alfonso,
and he sets them up along the bar, and Alfonso lights a
cigareller. So then the Don drinks, and the little red man
says, 'Salue.' And the little red man drinks, and Alfonso
says, 'Drink hearty.' And then they drinks two and two
together. Then Alfonso sings some sort of a Dago song,

and the little red man he plays a tune on the bones, and then they sets them up again and has more bones and more singing. Then Alfonso says, 'It's time I was gettin' aboard'; but the little man says, 'Oh, it's early days yet – the licker lies with you.' So every time Alfonso tries to go, the little red man says that. Till at last, at dawn, the little red man turned into a little red cock and crowed like a cock in the ox yard. And immejitly the corfins all burst into skellintons, and the bar broke into bits, and the licker blew up like corpse-lights – like blue fire, the same as in the scripters. And the next thing Don Alfonso knowed he was lying on the beach with a head on him full of mill-wheels and the mill working overtime.

So he gets up and sticks his head in the surf, and blows his whistle for the boat to come. But not a sign of a boat puts in, and not a sign of a hand shows aboard, neither smoke nor nothin'. So when he'd blew for maybe an hour he sees a old skellinton of a boat lying bilged on the sand. And he went off in her, paddling with the rudder, and he got alongside before she actually sank.

Now, when he gets alongside, that there brigantine was all rusty and rotted and all grown green with grass. And flowers were growing on the deck, and barnacles were a foot thick below the water. The gulls had nested in her sails, and the ropes drifted in the wind like flags, and a big red rose-bush was twisted up the tiller. And there in the grass, with daisies and such, were the lanky white bones of all them Dagoes. They lay where they'd died, with the vino casks near by and a pannikin of tin that they'd been using as a dicebox. They was dead white bones, the whole crew – dead of waiting for Don Alfonso while he was drinking with the little red man.

So Don Alfonso he kneels and he prays, and 'Oh,' he says, 'that I might die too, and me the cause of these here whited bones, and all from my love of licker! Never again will I touch rum,' he says. 'If I reach home,' he says – he was praying, you must mind – 'you'll see I never will.' And he hacks through the cable with an axe and runs up the rotten jib by pully-hauly.

Long he was sailing, living on dew and gulls' eggs, sailing with them white bones in that there blossoming old hulk. But at long last he comes to Port of Spain and signals for a pilot, and brings up just as sun was sinking. Thirty long years had he been gone, and he was an old man when he brought the whited bones home. But his old mother was alive, and they lived happily ever after. But never any licker would he drink, except only dew or milk – he was that changed from what he was.

PORT OF MANY SHIPS

'Down in the sea, very far down, under five miles of water, somewhere in the Gulf of Mexico, there is a sea cave, all roofed with coral. There is a brightness in the cave, although it is so far below the sea. And in the light there the great sea-snake is coiled in immense blue coils, with a crown of gold upon his horned head. He sits there very patiently from year to year, making the water tremulous with the threshing of his gills. And about him at all times swim the goggle-eyed dumb creatures of the sea. He is the king of all the fishes, and he waits there until the judgement day, when the waters shall pass away for ever and the dim kingdom disappear. At times the coils of his body wreathe themselves, and then the waters above him rage. One folding of his coil will cover a sea with shipwreck; and so it must be until the sea and the ships come to an end together in that serpent's death-throe.

'Now when that happens, when the snake is dying, there will come a lull and a hush, like when the boatswain pipes. And in that time of quiet you will hear a great beating of ships' bells, for in every ship sunken in the sea the life will go leaping to the white bones of the drowned. And every drowned sailor, with the weeds upon him, will spring alive again; and he will start singing and beating on the bells, as he did in life when starting out upon a cruise. And so great and sweet will be the music that they make that you will think little of harps from that time on, my son.

'Now the coils of the snake will stiffen out, like a rope

stretched taut for hauling. His long knobbed horns will droop. The golden crown will roll from his old, tired head. And he will lie there as dead as herring, while the sea will fall calm, like it was before the land appeared, with never a breaker in her. Then the great white whale, old Moby Dick, the king of all the whales, will rise up from his quiet in the sea, and go bellowing to his mates. And all the whales in the world – the spermwhales, the razor-back, the black-fish, the rorque, the right, the forty-barrel Jonah, the narwhal, the hump-back, the grampus and the thrasher – will come to him, "fin-out," blowing their spray to the heavens. Then Moby Dick will call the roll of them, and from all the parts of the sea, from the north, from the south, from Callao to Rio, not one whale will be missing. Then Moby Dick will trumpet, like a man blowing a horn, and all that company of whales will "sound" (that is, dive), for it is they that have the job of raising the wrecks from down below.

'Then when they come up the sun will just be setting in the sea, far away to the west, like a ball of red fire. And just as the curve of it goes below the sea, it will stop sinking and lie there like a door. And the stars and the earth and the wind will stop. And there will be nothing but the sea, and this red arch of the sun, and the whales with the wrecks, and a stream of light upon the water. Each whale will have raised a wreck from among the coral, and the sea will be thick with them – row-ships and sail-ships, and great big seventy-fours, and big White Star boats, and battleships, all of them green with the ooze, but all of them manned by singing sailors. And ahead of them will go Moby Dick, towing the ship our Lord was in, with all the sweet apostles aboard of her. And Moby Dick will give a great bellow, like a fog-horn blowing, and stretch "fin-out" for the sun away in the west. And all the whales will bellow out an answer. And all the drowned sailors will sing their chanties, and beat the bells into a music. And the whole fleet of them will start towing at full speed towards the sun, at the edge of the sky and water. I tell you they will make white water, those ships and fishes.

'When they have got to where the sun is, the red ball will swing open like a door, and Moby Dick, and all the whales, and all the ships will rush through it into an anchorage in Kingdom Come. It will be a great calm piece of water, with land close aboard, where all the ships of the world will lie at anchor, tier upon tier, with the hands gathered forward, singing. They'll have no watches to stand, no ropes to coil, no mates to knock their heads in. Nothing will be to do except singing and beating on the bell. And all the poor sailors who went in patched rags, my son, they'll be all fine in white and gold. And ashore, among the palm-trees, there'll be fine inns for the seamen, where you and I, maybe, will meet again, and I spin yarns, maybe, with no cause to stop until the bell goes.'

SEA SUPERSTITION

One moonlit night in the tropics, as my ship was slipping south under all sail, I was put to walking the deck on the lee side of the poop, with orders to watch the ship's clock and strike the bell at each half-hour. It was a duty I had done nightly for many nights, but this night was memorable to me. The ship was like a thing carved of pearl. The sailors, as they lay sleeping in the shadows, were like august things in bronze. And the skies seemed so near me, I felt as though we were sailing under a roof of dim branches, as of trees, that bore the moon and the stars like shining fruits.

Gradually, however, the peace in my heart gave way to an eating melancholy, and I felt a sadness, such as has come to me but twice in my life. With the sadness there came a horror of the water and of the skies, till my presence in that ship, under the ghastly corpse-light of the moon, among that sea, was a terror to me past power of words to tell. I went to the ship's rail, and shut my eyes for a moment, and then opened them to look down upon the water rushing past. I had shut my eyes upon the sea, but when I opened them I looked upon the forms of the sea-spirits. The water was indeed there, hurrying aft as the ship cut through; but in the bright foam for far about the ship I saw multitudes of beautiful, inviting faces that had an eagerness and a swiftness in them unlike the speed or the intensity of human beings. I remember thinking that I had never seen anything of such passionate beauty as those faces, and as I looked at them my melancholy fell away like a rag. I felt a longing to fling myself over the rail, so as to be with that inhuman beauty. Yet even as I looked that beauty became terrible, as the night had been terrible but a few seconds before. And with the changing of my emotions the faces changed. They became writhelled and hag-like: and in the leaping of the water, as we rushed, I saw malevolent white hands that plucked and snapped at me. I remember I was afraid to go near the rail again before the day dawned.

Not very long after that night, when I was sitting with a Danish sailor who was all broken on the wheel of his vices and not far from his death, I talked about the sea-spirits and their beauty and their wildness, feeling that such a haunted soul as my companion's would have room in its crannies for such wild birds. He told me much that was horrible about the ghosts who throng the seas. And it was he who gave me the old myth of the sea-gulls, telling me that the souls of old sailors follow the sea, in birds' bodies, till they have served their apprenticeship or purged their years of penitence. He told me of two sailors in a Norway barque, though I believe he lied when he said that he was aboard her at the time, who illustrated his sermon very aptly. The barque was going south from San Francisco, bound home round the Horn, and the two men were in the same watch. Somehow they fell to quarrelling as to which was the best dancer, and the one killed the other and flung him overboard during one of the night watches. The dead body did not sink, said my friend, because no body dares to sink to the undersea during the night-time; but in the dawn of the next day, and at the dawn of each day till the barque reached Norway, a white gull flew at the slayer, crying the cry of the gulls. It was the dead man's soul, my friend said, getting her revenge. The slayer gave himself up on his arrival at the home port, and took poison while awaiting trial.

When he had told me this tale, the Dane called for a tot of the raw spirits of that land, though he must have known, he being so old a sailor, that drink was poison to him. When he had swallowed the liquor, he began a story of one of his voyages to the States. He said that he was in a little English ship coming from New York to Hamburg, and that the ship – the winds being westerly – was making heavy running, under upper topsails, nearly all the voyage. When he was at the wheel with his mate (for two men steered in the pitch and hurry of that sailing) he was given to looking astern at the huge comber known as 'the following sea,' which topples up, green and grisly, astern of every ship with the wind aft. The sight of that water has a fascination for all men, and it fascinated him, he said, till he thought he saw in the shaking wave the image of an old halt man who came limping, bent on a crutch, in the ship's wake. So vivid was the image of that cripple, he leaned across the wheel-box to his mate, bidding him to look; and his mate looked, and immediately went white to the lips, calling to the saints to preserve him. My friend then told me that the cripple only appears to ships foredoomed to shipwreck, 'And,' he said, 'we were run down in the Channel and sunk in ten minutes' by a clumsy tramp from London.

After a while I left that country in a steamer whose sailors were of nearly every nation under the sun, and from a Portuguese aboard her I got another yarn. In the night watches, when I was alone on the poop, I used to lean on the taffrail to see the water reeling away from the screws. While loafing in this way one night, a little while before the dawn, I was joined by the Portuguese, an elderly, wizened fellow, who wore earrings. He said he had often seen me leaning over the taffrail, and had come to warn me that there was danger in looking upon the sea in that way. Men who looked into the water, he told me, would at first see only the bubbles, and the eddies, and the foam. Then they would see dim pictures of themselves and of the ship. But at the last they always saw some unholy thing, and the unholy thing would lure them away to death. And it was a danger, he said, no young man should face, for though the other evil spirits, those of the earth and air, had power only upon the body, the evil spirits of the sea were deadly to the soul. There was a lad he had known in Lisbon who had gone along the coast in a brig, and this lad was always looking into the sea, and had at last seen the unholy things and flung his body to them across the rail. The brig was too near the coast, and it blew too freshly inshore, for the sailors to round-to to pick him up. But they found the lad in Lisbon when they got home. He said he had sunken down into the sea, till the sea opened about him and showed him a path among a field of green corn. He had gone up the path and come at last to a beautiful woman, surrounded by many beautiful women, but the one seemed to him to be the queen. She was so beautiful, he said, the sight of her was like strong wine; but she shook her head when she saw him, as though she could never give him her love, and immediately he was at the surface, under the skies, struggling towards some rocks a little distance from him. He reached the shore and went home to Lisbon in a fisher-boat, but he was never quite sane after seeing that beauty beneath the sea. He became very melancholy, and used to go down the Tagus in a row-boat, singing to himself and looking down into the water.

Before I left that ship I had to help clean her for her decent entry to the Mersey. I spent one afternoon with an old man from the Clyde doing up some ironwork, first with rope yarn and paraffin, then with red lead. The mate left us to ourselves all the watch, because the old man was trusty, and we had a fine yarn together about the things of the sea. He said that there were some who believed in the white whale, though it was all folly their calling him the king of all the fishes. The white whale was nothing but a servant, and lay low, 'somewhere nigh the Poles,' till the last day dawned. And then, said the old man, 'he's a busy man raising the wrecks.' When I asked him who was the king of all the fishes, he looked about to see that there were no listeners, and said, in a very earnest voice, that the king of the fish was the sea-serpent. He lies coiled, said the old man, in the hot waters of the Gulf, with a gold crown on his head, and a 'great sleep upon him,' waiting till the setting of the last sun. 'And then?' I asked. 'Ah, then,' he answered, 'there'll be fine times going for us sailors.'

A SAILOR'S YARN

'Once upon a time there was a clipper ship called the *Mary*, and she was lying in Panama waiting for a freight. It was hot, and it was calm, and it was hazy, and the men aboard her were dead sick of the sight of her. They had been lying there all the summer, having nothing to do but to wash her down, and scrape the royal masts with glass, and make the chain cables bright. And aboard of her was a big AB from Liverpool, with a tattooed chest on him and an arm like a spar. And this man's name was Bill.

'Now, one day, while the captain of this clipper was sunning in the club, there came a merchant to him offering him a fine freight home and "despatch" in loading. So the old man went aboard that evening in a merry temper, and bade the mates rastle the hands aft. He told them that they could go ashore the next morning for a "liberty-day" of four-and-twenty hours, with twenty dollars pay to blue, and no questions asked if they came aboard drunk. So forward goes all hands merrily, to rout out their go-ashore things, their red handkerchiefs, and "sombre-airers", for to astonish the Dons. And ashore they goes the next morning, after breakfast, with their silver dollars in their fists, and the jolly-boat to take them. And ashore they steps, and "So long" they says to the young fellows in the boat, and so up the Mole to the beautiful town of Panama.

'Now the next morning that fellow Bill I told you of was tacking down the city to the boat, singing some song or another. And when he got near to the jetty he went fumbling in his pocket for his pipe, and what should he find but a silver dollar that had slipped away and been saved. So he thinks. "If I go aboard with this dollar, why the hands'll laugh at me; besides, it's a wasting of it not to spend it." So he cast about for some place where he could blue it in.

'Now close by where he stood there was a sort of a great store, kept by a Johnny Dago. And if I were to tell you of the things they had in it, I would need nine tongues and an oiled hinge to each of them. But Billy walked into this store, into the space inside, into like the 'tween decks, for to have a look about him before buying. And there were great bunches of bananas a-ripening against the wall. And stacks of dried raisins, and bags of dried figs, and melon seeds, and pomegranates enough to sink you. Then there were cotton bales, and calico, and silk of Persia. And rum in puncheons, and bottled ale. And all manner of sweets, and a power of a lot of chemicals. And anchors gone rusty, fished up from the bay after the ships were gone. And spare cables, all ranged for letting go. And ropes, and sails, and balls of marline stuff. Then there was blocks of all kinds, wood and iron. Dunnage there was, and scantling, likewise sea-chests with pictures on them. And casks of beef and pork, and paint, and peas, and petrolium. But for not one of these things did Billy care a handful of bilge.

'Then there were medical comforts, such as ginger and calavances. And plug tobacco, and coil tobacco, and tobacco leaf, and tobacco clippings. And such a power of a lot of bulls' hides as you never saw. Likewise there was tinned things like cocoa, and boxed things like China tea. And any quantity of blankets, and rugs, and donkeys' breakfasts. And oilskins there was, and rubber sea-boots, and shore shoes, and Crimee shirts. Also Dungarees, and soap, and matches, so many as you never heard tell. But no, not for one of these things was Bill going for to bargain.

'Then there were lamps and candles, and knives and

nutmeg-graters, and things made of bright tin and saucers of red clay; and rolls of coloured cloth, made in the hills by the Indians. Bowls there were, painted with twisty-whirls by the folk of old time. And flutes from the tombs (of the Incas), and whistles that looked like flower-pots. Also fiddles and beautiful melodeons. Then there were paper roses for ornament, and false white flowers for graves; also paint-brushes and coir-brooms. There were cages full of parrots, both green and grey; and white cockatoos on perches a-nodding their red crests; and Java lovebirds a-billing, and parrakeets a-screaming, and little kittens for the ships with rats. And at the last of all there was a little monkey, chained to a sack of jib-hanks, who sat upon his tail a-grinning.

'Now Bill he sees this monkey, and he thinks he never see a cuter little beast, not never. And then he thinks of something, and he pipes up to the old Johnny Dago, and he says, pointing to the monkey:

' "Hey-a Johnny! How much-a take-a little munk?"

'So the old Johnny Dago looks at Bill a spell, and then says:

' "I take-a five-a doll' that-a little munk."

'So Billy planks down his silver dollar, and says:

' "I give-a one doll', you cross-eyed Dago."

'Then the old man unchained the monkey, and handed him to Bill without another word. And away the pair of them went, down the Mole to where the boats lay, where a lanchero took them off to the *Mary*.

'Now when they got aboard all hands came around Bill, saying: "Why, Bill, whatever are you going to do with that there little monkey?" And Bill he said: "You shut your heads about that there little monkey. I'm going to teach that little monkey how to speak. And when he can speak I'm going to sell him to a museum. And then I'll buy a farm. I won't come to sea any more." So they just laugh at

Bill, and by and by the *Mary* loaded, and got her hatches on, and sailed south-away, on the road home to Liverpool.

'Well, every evening, in the dog-watch, after supper, while the decks were drying from the washing-down, Bill used to take the monkey on to the fo'c's'le head, and set him on the capstan. "Well, ye little divvle," he used to say, "will ye speak? Are ye going to speak, hey?" and the monkey would just grin and chatter back at Billy, but never no Christian speech came in front of them teeth of his. And this game went on until they were up with the Horn, in bitter cold weather, running east like a stag, with a great sea piling up astern. And then one night, at eight bells, Billy came on deck for the first watch, bringing the monkey with him. It was blowing like sin, stiff and cold, and the *Mary* was butting through, and dipping her fo'c's'le under. So Bill takes the monkey, and lashes him down good and snug on the drum of the capstan, on the fo'c's'le head. "Now, you little divvle," he said, "will you speak? Will you speak, eh?" But the monkey just grinned at him.

'At the end of the first hour he came again. "Are ye going to speak, ye little beggar?" he says, and the monkey sits and shivers, but never a word does the little beggar say. And it was the same at four bells, when the look-out man was relieved. But at six bells Billy came again, and the monkey looked mighty cold, and it was a wet perch where he was roosting, and his teeth chattered; yet he didn't speak, not so much as a cat. So just before eight bells, when the watch was nearly out, Billy went forward for the last time. "If he don't speak now," says Billy, "overboard he goes for a dumb animal."

'Well, the cold green seas had pretty nearly drowned that little monkey. And the sprays had frozen him over like a jacket of ice, and right blue his lips were, and an icicle was a-dangling from his chin, and he was shivering like he

23

had an ague. "Well, ye little divvle," says Billy, "for the last time, will ye speak? Are ye going to speak, hey?" And the monkey spoke. "*Speak* is it? *Speak* is it?" he says. "It's so cold it's enough to make a little fellow *swear*."

'It's the solemn gospel truth that story is.'

THE YARN OF LANKY JOB

Lanky Job was a lazy Bristol sailor, notorious for his sleepiness throughout the seven seas. And though many captains had taken him in hand, none had ever made him spryer, or got more than a snail's work out of him. Perhaps he would have been more wakeful had he not been born with a caul, which preserved him at sea from any danger of drowning. Often he had fallen from aloft or from the forecastle rail while dreaming during his work or look-out. But his captains had always paused to pick him up, and to all his captains he had made a graceful speech of thanks which ended with a snore at the ninth or tenth word.

One day he was lolling on a bollard on the quay at Bristol as fast asleep as man could wish. He had fallen asleep in the forenoon, but when he woke the sun was setting, and right in front of him moored to the quay, was the most marvellous ship that ever went through water. She was bluff-bowed and squat, with a great castle in her bows and five poops, no less, one above the other, at her starn. And outside her bulwarks there were painted screens, all scarlet and blue and green, with ships painted on them, and burning birds and ladies in cloth of gold. And then above them were rows of hammocks covered with a white piece of linen. And every little poop had a rail. And her buckets were green, and in every bucket there were roses growing. And the masts were of ebony with mast-rings of silver. And her decks were all done in parquet-work in green and white woods, and the man who did the caulking had caulked the deck-seams with red tar, for he was a master of his trade. And the cabins was all glorious to behold with carving, and sweet to smell, like oranges. And right astern she carried a great gold lantern with a big blue banner underneath it, and an ivory staff to the whole, all carved by a Chinaman.

So Job looks at the ship, and he thinks he never see a finer, so he ups alongside, and along a gangway, and there he sees a little sea captain with a big red hat and feather, and a silver whistle to him, walking on the quarter-deck.

'Good morning, Job,' says the little sea captain, 'and how dy'ye like my ship?'

'Sir,' says Job, 'I never see a finer.'

So the little sea captain takes Job forrard and gives him a bite in the forecastle, and then takes him aft and gives him a sup in the cabin.

'And Job,' he says, 'how would ye like to sail aboard this beautiful ship?'

So Job, who was all wide awake with the beauty of her, he says:

'Oh, sir, I'd like it of all things; she be so comely to see.'

And immediately he said that, Job see the little captain pipe his whistle, and a lot of little sailors in red hats ran up and cast her hawsers off. And then the sheets sheeted home of themselves and the ship swung away from Bristol, and there was Job nodding on the quarter-deck, a mile out to sea, the ship running west like a deer.

'You'll be in the port watch,' said the little captain to him, 'and woe betide you, Lanky Job, if we catch you asleep in your watch.'

Now Job never knowed much about that trip of his among them little men in red hats, but he knowed he slept once, and they stuck needles in him. And he knowed he slept twice, and they stuck hot pokers in him. And he knowed he slept a third time, and 'Woe betide you, Lanky Job,' they said, and they set him on the bowsprit end, with bread in one hand and a sup of water in the other. 'And stay you there, Lanky Job,' they said, ''till you drop into the sea and drown.'

Now pitiful was his case truly, for if he looked behind there was little red men to prick him, and if he looked before he got giddy, and if he looked down he got sick, and if he looked up he got dazzled. So he looked all four ways and closed his eyes, and down he toppled from his perch, going splash into the wash below the bows. 'And now for a sleep,' he says, 'since there's no water wet enough to drown me.' And asleep he falls, and long does he drift in the sea.

Now, by and by, when he had floated for quite a while, he sees a big ship, black as pitch, with heavy red sails, come sailing past him in the dawn. And although he had a caul and couldn't be drowned, he was glad enough to see that ship, and right glad indeed to clutch her braces as she rolled. She came swooping down on him, and he caught her main brace as she lay down to leeward from a gust. And with her windward roll and a great heave, he just managed to reach her deck before he fell asleep again. He noticed as he scrambled up the side that she was heavily barnacled, and that she had forty boats to a broadside, all swinging on ivory davits.

But when he woke from his sleep, lo and behold, the ship was manned by nothing but great rats, and they were all in blue clothes like sailors, and snarling as they swung the yards. And as soon as they saw Lanky Job they came around him, gnashing their long yellow teeth and twirling their hairy whiskers. And the multitude of them was beyond speech, and at every moment it seemed to Job that a boat came alongside with more of them, till the decks were ropy with their tails. Six or seven of them seized hold of him and dragged him aft to where a big bone tiller swung, with a helmsman on each side of it, seated in heavy golden chairs. These helmsmen were half men, half rats, and they were hairy like rats, and grey like rats, and they had rats' eyes. But they had the minds of men, and they were the captains of that hooker, and right grim they were to look at. Now when he sees those grim things sitting there, Job knew that he'd come aboard the rat flag-ship, whose boats row every sea, picking up the rats as they leave ships going to sink. And he gave a great scream and punched out at the gang who held him, and over the side he bounded. And he drifted a day and a night, till the salt-cracks were all over his body, and he came ashore half dead at Avonmouth, having been a week away. But always after that Lanky Job was a spry sailor, as smart as you could find anywheres.

FROM THE SPANISH

The galleon *Spanish Rose* was built in Saint Mary of the
Bells by the Lord Alva of Meroquinez. He built her for one
of the beauties of the court, whom he loved in a stately
manner, that was ceremonious, like the worship of a relic.
Being a rich man he built her of costly things, of cedar-
wood from the East, of Indian rosewood, so that each
plank of her was sweet to smell. Her fastenings were of
wrought silver, curiously beaten. The streets of the silver
workers rang noisily for a twelvemonth over the lovely
hammering of them. Her decks were beautifully inlaid by
the parquetters of Verona, who made in them delicate
patterns of coloured woods more brilliant than the sea-
weeds. The figure-head, carved in a hard wood, was the
work of that artist who carved the Madonna in St James's
Church at Seville. It was a design of the Rosa Dei,
bursting her golden petals that the cross might show, a
rare piece, sweetly wrought; the folk came far to see it. Her
sails were of a fine bleached canvas, edged with red
Cordoba leather. They bore a wreathed intricacy of roses,
embroidered in crimson or yellow silk by the ladies of
Meroquinez. The roping was of that precious hemp which
grows only on the Sacred Hill (in Igorroti, in Luzon), so
that an ell of it was worth a Florence crown by the time it
reached the Spanish riggers' hands. Her high stern, that
was built in three decks, had painted bulwarks, each of
which bore some painted history of the sea, each history
by some Italian.

There one might see Ulysses, in his red-beaked galley,

29

as he rowed past those piping trulls the sirens. There was the barge of Antony, hung with purple, taking the Egyptian beauty along Nilus. There was Saint Brandan Bright Hair, in his curragh of holy wood, with his singing monks about him. There was the fishing-boat of Peter, that was long worshipped by the Galileans when the spring fisheries were in hand. There was the Genoan in his bark, his yellow banner blowing out bravely. There was Arion at his luting. There were the strange sailors of Atlantis, the seven brothers that loved the merrows of the sea, as the Arabian poet has set down. Also there was painted lively the great Flood, with green waves running fiercely, tossing the Ark skyward. Opposite thereto was a table of the Last Day, the sea stilled, with drowned mariners, made glorious, ascending in triumph to the harping of sainted hosts. Within her, in her cabins, she was wrought with more beautiful things. For in the decks of the cabins were roses, worked in parquetry of scarlet log-wood, with green leaves, in stained fir, surrounding the heavy blossoms. The bulkheads were of precious wood, carven in pilasters that had gilded roses at their tops. There was a painting on each cabin wall, of Elizabeth with her roses, of Mary in the flowered field, or of those other hallows that have the rose as their symbol. The doorways were hung with blue arras of Persia, or with grey tapestry, splendid with purple peacocks, from the nuns' looms at Ephrata. Each cabin was lit with a silver lamp, that swung in gimbals above a mirror. In every cabin was a silver crucifix, above an old censer of flowered copper, studded with jewels, which sent up scented smoke at every canonical hour. The cabin beams were painted in designs of flowers, but always of red or crimson flowers, such as the rose or poppy, to symbolize love in her activity or weakness. Inlaid upon certain parts of the walls, such as those at the carved bed's head, were curious transcripts from Holy Writ, in praise of love, or verses of the amorous poets, such as Ovid or Petrarch. In each cabin was a cabinet, like a reliquary for richness, containing the precious books of love, written upon vellum, in coloured inks, by fine penmen to whom art was a religion. There might you see Messer Dante, or some rare scroll sealed in red wax, written in Greek, with the tale of Psyche. These books were bound in a green leather, to signify their immortality, while on the cover of each book some jeweller had fashioned a rose in tiny rubies, that typified the love of the saints.

Now about the decks of this wondrous galleon were stands of curious armour, all scrupulously bright. At her ports, which had every one a wreath of painted roses round it, were cannon of polished brass that shone like gold. Above these were the close fights, or strips of canvas, running the length of the deck, all curiously painted with the Lord Alva's arms, in a design of coloured shields that showed the blazonings of his family. The mariners were all Spaniards from Boca Gara, the little port of Meroquinez fronting the Atlantic. The soldiers were but few in number, some twenty swords from Estremadura, who had been in the Indies under Oviedo. They wore bright armour inlaid with gold. In their helmets they wore jewels, or gloves, or feathers, that were the gifts of ladies whom they had served. Their sword-belts were of green leather, in token of hope. Their swords had, every blade of them, drawn blood in the defence of beauty. If I had the pens of twenty poets I might not tell the glory of the stately life they lived, on board the *Spanish Rose*, the ship built for the Lord Alva's lady. For, in lieu of the exercises common to soldiers or shipmen, they would gather about the mast to hear some pleasant singing in praise of love by one of the Provençal poets, of whom the ship carried nine. Or the lutenists would take their viols, playing some sweet music that for its beauty was like a woman's hair. In the twilights, at Boca Gara, while the ship was fitting for the sea, those on board of her would gather at the mast, with their censers, to sing their vespers, at the first rising of the evening star.

At night, when the moon was up, some of the mariners, coming from the mysterious darkness in the bows, would light the lantern on the poop, a lantern shaped like a rose. The glass of it was stained crimson, so that when lit it burned like a red rose through the darkness, a sight passing a rose in beauty. All of these amorous subtleties, all of this extravagance of beauty, was for the Lady Alathe of Ayamonte, the woman whom Lord Alva loved. He had courted her during the months while the ship was being fitted for sea; for he had vowed to bring his bride home to Meroquinez, by water, in a ship fitting her birth. When the *Spanish Rose* was ready, her crew on board, her bows blessed by the priests, she sailed out from Boca Gara to a noise of singing that mingled with the bells of St Mary's Church. She reached Ayamonte after three weeks' sailing along the coast, anchoring one sunny afternoon beneath the blossomed orange groves which scent the houses of the port. He was married the next day at the cathedral, while all the bells in the town rang as they ring at Easter, in exultation. After a solemn leave-taking he set sail again (his bride with him) for his home at St Mary of the Bells.

There are nine rocks, submerged at high water, about a league to the south-east of Ayamonte Harbour. They go by the name of the Nine Drowned Maidens. They are a menace to shipping, but latterly they have been marked by a lighthouse. It is thought that the Lord Alva's pilot had been made merry with Greek wine (though some say the ill-steering was done by a knight of the bride's company, who loved the lady too well to suffer her to belong to another). At any rate the *Spanish Rose* struck upon the rocks during the noontime, when her gay complement, so like a bed of tulips for brilliant colour, were drinking to the lady's health. She sank in less than a minute, in deep, calm blue water, with all her company on board. All that was saved of her was an Italian lute, strung with gay, silk ribbons, which floated ashore the next day.

Less than ten years ago, when the Ayamonte folk were laying the foundations for their lighthouse, a diver came upon some weeded wreck of her, fairly well preserved, lying on the sand, with a sort of grey silt spreading over her like a cloak. He recovered a few relics from her, such as bits of timber, brass nails, or rusty ironwork, which may be seen at the town museum to this day. The scheme for raising her fell through for lack of funds, but it may be that some American millionaire, greedy of dollars, will form a company to strip the wreck. Perhaps some poor Spanish diver, thrusting through into her central-cabin, will then come across the bones of those great lovers, in the perished magnificence of their bridal banquet, their bony hands still clutching the cups, their whitened fingers still splendid with the wedding rings.

THE SEAL MAN

'The seals is pretty when they do be playing,' said the old woman. 'Ah, I seen them frisking their tails till you'd think it was rocks with the seas beating on them, the time the storm's on. I seen the merrows of the sea sitting yonder on the dark stone, and they had crowns on them, and they were laughing. The merrows is not good; it's not good to see too many of them. They are beautiful like young men in their shirts playing hurley. They're as beautiful as anything you would be seeing in Amerikey or Australeyey, or any place. The seals is beautiful too, going through the water in the young of the day; but they're not so beautiful as them. The seals is no good either. It's a great curse keeps them the way they are, not able to live either in the sea or on the land.

'One time there was a man of the O'Donnells came here, and he was a bad man. A saint in Heaven would have been bothered to find good in him. He died of the fever that came before the Famine. I was a girl then; and if you'd seen the people in them times; there wasn't enough to bury them. The pigs used to eat them in the loanings. And their mouths would be all green where they'd eaten grass from want of food. If you'd seen the houses there was then, indeed, you'd think the place bewitched. But the cabins is all fell in, like wonder, and there's no dancing or fiddling, or anything at all, and all of my friends is gone to Amerikey or Australeyey; I've no one at all to bury me, unless it's that humpy one who comes here, and she's as proud as a Jew. She's no cause to be proud, with a hump

34

on her; her father was just a poor man, the same as any.

'This O'Donnell I was telling you. My father was at his wake. And they'd the candles lit, and they were drinking putcheen. My father was nearest the door, and a fear took him, and he got up, with his glass in his hand, and he cried out: "There's something here is not good." And another of them said: "There's something wants to get out." And another said: "It's himself wants to go out into the dark night." And another said: "For the love of God, open the door." So my father flung the door open; and, outside, the moon shone down to the sea. And the corpse of the O'Donnell was all blue, and it got up with the sheet knotted on it, and walked out without leaving a track. So they followed it, saying their prayers to Almighty God, and it walked on down to the sea. And when it came to the edge of the sea, the sea was like a flame before it. And it bowed there, three times; and each time it rose up it screamed. And all the seals, and all the merrows, and all them that's under the tides, they came up to welcome it. They called out to the corpse and laughed; and the corpse laughed back, and fell on to the sand. My father and the other men saw the wraith pass from it, into the water, as it fell. It was like a little black boy, laughing, with great long arms on him. It was all bald and black; and its hands moved like he was tickling someone.

'And after that the priest had him buried, like they buried the Old Ones; but the wraith passed into a bull seal. You would be feared to see the like of the bull seal. There was a man of the O'Kanes fired a blessed shilling at him, and the seal roared up at him and tore his arms across. There was marks like black stars on him after till he died. And the bull seal walked like a man at the change of the moon, like a big, tall, handsome man stepping the roads. You'd be feared, sir, if you saw the like. He set his

35

eyes on young Norah O'Hara. Lovely she was. She'd little ways, sir, would draw the heart out of an old bachelor. Wasn't it a great curse he should take her when there was old hags the like of Mary that has no more beauty than a withered broom that you wouldn't be bothered to mend or a done-out old gather-up of a duck that a hungry dog would blush to be biting? Still, he took Norah.

'She had a little son, and the little son was a seal-man; the priest wouldn't sign him with the cross. When Norah died he used always to be going to the sea; he would always be swimming. He'd little soft brown hair, like a seal's, the prettiest you would be seeing. He used to talk to the seals. My father was coming home one night from Carnmore, and he saw the little seal-man in the sea; and the seals were playing with him, singing songs. But my father was feared to hear; he ran away. They stoned the seal-man, whiles, after that; but whiles they didn't stone it. They had a kindness for it, although it had no holy water on it. It was a very young thing to be walking the world, and it was a beautiful wee thing, with its eyes so pretty; so it grew up to be a man.

'Them that live in the water, they have ways of calling people. Them who pass this seal-man, they felt the call in their hearts. Indeed, if you passed the seal-man, stepping the roads, you would get a queer twist from the way he looked at you. And he set his love on a young girl of the O'Keefe's, a little young girl with no more in her than the flower on its stalk. You would see them in the loanings coming home, or in the bright of the day going. There was a strong love was on them two young things; it was like the love of the Old Ones that took nine deaths to kill. They would be telling Kate it was not right she should set her love on one who wasn't like ourselves; but there's few indeed is the young'll listen. They are all for pleasure, all for pleasure, before they are withered old hags, the like of my sister Mary. And at last they shut her up at home, to keep her from seeing him. And he came by her cabin to the west of the road, calling. There was a strong love came up in her at that, and she put down her sewing on the table, and "Mother," she says, "there's no lock, and no key, and no bolt, and no door. There's no iron, nor no stone, nor anything at all will keep me this night from the man I love." And she went out into the moonlight to him, there by the bush where the flowers is pretty, beyond the river. And he says to her: "You are all of the beauty of the world, will you come where I go, over the waves of the sea?" And she says to him: "My treasure and my strength," she says, "I would follow you on the frozen hills, my feet bleeding."

'Then they went down into the sea together, and the moon made a track upon the sea, and they walked down it; it was like a flame before them. There was no fear at all on her; only a great love like the love of the Old Ones, that was stronger than the touch of the fool. She had a little white throat, and little cheeks like flowers, and she went down into the sea with her man, who wasn't a man at all. She was drowned, of course. It's like he never thought that she wouldn't bear the sea like himself. She was drowned, drowned.

'When it come light they saw the seal-man sitting yonder on the rock, and she lying by him, dead, with her face as white as a flower. He was crying and beating her hands to bring life to her. It would have drawn pity from a priest to hear him, though he wasn't Christian. And at last, when he saw that she was drowned, he took her in his arms and slipped into the sea like a seal. And he swam, carrying her, with his head up, laughing and laughing and laughing, and no one ever saw him again at all.'

THE WESTERN ISLANDS

'Once there were two sailors; and one of them was Joe, and
the other one was Jerry, and they were fishermen. And
they'd a young apprentice-feller, and his name was Jim.
And Joe was a great one for his pot, and Jerry was a
wonder at his pipe; and Jim did all the work, and both
of them banged him. So one time Joe and Jerry were
in the beerhouse, and there was a young parson there,
telling the folk about foreign things, about plants and
that. "Ah," he says, "what wonders there are in the
west."

'"What sort of wonders, begging your pardon, sir,"
says Joe. "What sort of wonders might them be?"

'"Why, all sorts of wonders," says the parson. "Why, in
the west," he says, "there's things you wouldn't believe.
No, you wouldn't believe; not till you'd seen them," he
says. "There's diamonds growing on trees. And great,
golden, glittering pearls as common as pea-straw. And
there's islands in the west. Ah, I could tell you of them.
Islands? I rather guess there's islands. None of your Isles
of Man. None of your Alderney and Sark. Not in them
seas."

'"What sort of islands might they be, begging your
pardon, sir?" says Jerry.

'"Why, the parson feller says, "ISLANDS. Islands as big
as Spain. Islands with rivers of rum and streams of
sarsaparilla. And none of your roses. Rubies and ame-
thynes is all the roses grows in them parts. With golden
stalks to them, and big diamond sticks to them, and the

taste of pork-crackling if you eat them. They're the sort of roses to have in your area," he says.

' "And what else might there be in them parts, begging your pardon, sir?" says Joe.

' "Why," he says, this parson says, "there's wonders. There's not only wonders, but miracles. And not only miracles, but sperrits."

' "What sort of sperrits might they be, begging your pardon?" says Jerry. "Are they rum and that?"

' "When I says sperrits," says the parson feller, "I mean ghosts."

' "Of course ye do," says Joe.

' "Yes, ghosts," says the parson. "And by ghosts I mean sperrits. And by sperrits I mean white things. And by white things I mean things as turn your hair white. And there's red devils there, and blue devils there, and a great gold queen a-waiting for a man to kiss her. And the first man as dares to kiss that queen, why he becomes king, and all her sacks of gold become his."

' "Begging your pardon, sir," said Jerry, "but whereabouts might these here islands be?"

' "Why, in the west," says the parson. "In the west, where the sun sets."

' "Ah," said Joe and Jerry. "What wonders there are in the world."

* * *

'Now, after that, neither one of them could think of anything but these here western islands. So at last they take their smack, and off they go in search of them. And Joe had a barrel of beer in the bows, and Jerry had a box of twist in the waist, and pore little Jim stood and steered abaft all. And in the evenings Jerry and Joe would bang their pannikins together, and sing of the great times they

39

meant to have when they were married to the queen. Then they would clump pore little Jim across the head, and tell him to watch out, and keep her to her course, or they'd ride him down like you would a main tack. And he'd better mind his eye, they told him, or they'd make him long to be boiled and salted. And he'd better put more sugar in the tea, they said, or they'd cut him for cod-bait. And who was he, they asked, to be wanting meat for dinner, when there was that much weevilly biscuit in the bread-barge? And boys was going to the dogs, they said, when limbs the like of him had the heaven-born insolence to want to sleep. And a nice pass things was coming to, they said, when a lad as they'd done everything for, and saved, so to speak, from the workhouse, should go for to snivel when they hit him a clip. If they'd said a word, when they was hit, when they was boys, they told him, they'd have had their bloods drawed, and been stood in the wind to cool. But let him take heed, they said, and be a good lad, and do the work of five, and they wouldn't half wonder, they used to say, as he'd be a man before his mother. So the sun shone, and the stars came out golden, and all the sea was a sparkle of gold with them. Blue was the sea, and the wind blew, too, and it blew Joe and Jerry west as fast as a cat can eat sardines.

*   *   *

'And one fine morning the wind fell calm, and a pleasant smell came over the water, like nutmegs on a rum-milk-punch. Presently the dawn broke. And, lo and behold, a rousing great wonderful island, all scarlet with coral and with rubies. The surf that was beating on her sands went shattering into silver coins, into dimes, and pesetas, and francs, and fourpenny bits. And the flowers on the cliffs was all one gleam and glitter. And the beauty of that island was a beauty beyond the beauty of Sally Brown, the lady as kept the beer-house. And on the beach of that island, on a golden throne, like, sat a woman so lovely that to look at her was as good as a church-service for one.

'"That's the party I got to kiss," said Jerry. "Steady, and beach her, Jim, boy," he says. "Run her ashore, lad. That's the party is to be my queen."

'"You've got a neck on you, all of a sudden," said Joe. "You ain't the admiral of this fleet. Not by a wide road you ain't. I'll do all the kissing as there's any call for. You keep clear, my son."

'The boat ran her nose into the sand, and the voyagers went ashore. The talk continued.

'"Keep clear, is it?" said Jerry. "You tell me to keep clear? You tell me again, and I'll put a head on you 'll make you sing like a kettle. Who are you to tell me to keep clear?"

'"I tell you who I am," said Joe. "I'm a better man than you are. That's what I am. I'm Joe the Tank, from Limehouse Basin, and there's no tinker's donkey-boy'll make me stand from under. Who are you to go kissing queens? Who are you that talk so proud and so mighty? You've a face on you would make a Dago tired. You look like a sea-sick Kanaka that's boxed seven rounds with a buzz-saw. You've no more manners than a hog, and you've a lip on you would fetch the enamel off a cup."

'"If it comes to calling names," said Jerry, "you ain't the only pebble on the beach. Whatever you might think, I tell you you ain't. You're the round turn and two-half hitches of a figure of fun as makes the angels weep. That's what you are. And you're the right-hand strand, and the left-hand strand, and the centre strand, and the core, and the serving, and the marling, of a three-stranded, left-handed, poorly worked junk of a half begun and never finished odds and ends of a Port Mahon soldier. You look like a Portuguese drummer. You've a whelky red nose that

shines like a port side-light. You've a face like a muddy
field where they've been playing football in the rain. Your
hair is an insult and a shame. I blush when I look at you.
You give me a turn like the first day out to a first voyager.
Kiss, will you? Kiss? Man, I tell you you'd paralyse a
shark if you kissed him. Paralyse him, strike him cold.
That's what a kiss of yours'd do."

' "You ought to a been a parson," said Joe, "that's
what you'd ought. There's many would a paid you for talk
like that. But for all your fine talk, and for all your dandy
language, you'll not come the old soldier over me. No, nor
ten of you. *You* talk of kissing, when there's a handsome
young man, the likes of me, around? Neither you nor ten of
you. To hear you talk one'd think you was a Emperor or a
Admiral. One would think you was a Bishop or a King.
One might mistake you for a General or a Member of
Parliament. You might. Straight, you might. A General or
a Bishop or a King. And what are you? What are you? I
ask you plain. What are you? – I'll tell you what you are.

' "You're him as hired himself out as a scarecrow, acos
no one'd take you as a fo'c's'le hand. You're him as give
the colic to a weather-cock. You're him as turned old
Mother Bomby's beer. You're him as drowned the duck
and stole the monkey. You're him as got the medal
give him for having a face that made the bull tame.
You're –"

' "Now don't you cast no more to me," said Jerry. "For
I won't take no lip from a twelve-a-shilling, cent-a-corner,
the likes of you are. You're the clippings of old junk, what
the Dagoes smokes in cigarettes. A swab, and a wash-
deck-broom, and the half of a pint of paint'd make a
handsomer figer of a man than what you are. I've seen a
coir whisk, what they grooms a mule with, as had a
sweeter face than you got. So stand aside, before you're
put aside. I'm the king of this here island. You can go

chase yourself for another. Stand clear, I say, or I'll give you a jog'll make your bells ring."

* * *

'Now, while they were argufying, young Jim, the young apprentice feller, he creeps up to the queen upon the throne. She was beautiful, she was, and she shone in the sun, and she looked straight ahead of her like a wax-work in a show. And in her hand she had a sack full of jewels, and at her feet she had a sack full of gold, and by her side was an empty throne ready for the king she married. But round her right hand there was a red snake, and round her left hand there was a blue snake, and the snakes hissed and twisted, and they showed their teeth full of poison. So Jim looked at the snakes, and he hit them a welt, right and left, and he kissed the lady.

'And immediately all the bells and the birds of the world burst out a-ringing and a-singing. The lady awoke from her sleep, and Jim's old clothes were changed to cloth of gold. And there he was, a king, on the throne beside the lady.

'But the red snake turned to a big red devil who took a hold of Joe, and the blue snake turned to a big blue devil, who took a hold of Jerry. And "Come you here, you brawling pugs," they said, "come and shovel sand." And Joe and Jerry took the spades that were given to them. And "Dig, now," said the devils. "Heave round. Let's see you dig. Dig, you scarecrows. And tell us when you've dug to London."'

CAPTAIN JOHN WARD

Captain John Ward, our 'most notorious pirate,' was born at Feversham, in Kent, about the year 1555. We first hear of him as a fisherman of that town, the child of mean parents, of 'estate lowe', and of 'hope', or expectations, still less. It has been stated that, at one time, presumably in his youth, he made one of a buccaneering party in the West Indies. It is highly probable that he learned the crafts of seamanship and navigation as a mariner in one of the many raids against the Spaniards, between the years 1570 and 1596. The Spanish Main, no less than the English Channel at that time, was a very pleasant place for a pirate; and Ward, in later years, talked mournfully of the good days he had had in his youth, 'robbing at will, and counting the world but a garden where he walked for sport.' After the death of Drake, in 1596, he seems to have been a seaman aboard one of the Queen's ships on a voyage to Portugal. Pepwell, writing in 1608, tells us that he 'rose through all ranks of the (naval) service in our wars with Spain.'

His buccaneering and naval service, if he ever indulged in any, failed to make his fortune; for he was a fisherman at Feversham, owning a single small fishing-boat, in the year 1602. In that year his pride grew to such a height that he could brook the fishery no longer. 'Nothing would serve him but the wide Ocean to walke in.' He went aboard his ketch one morning, and crept along the coast to Plymouth, where he seems to have sold his vessel for a fair sum. His wife he left behind him at Feversham.

For the next few months he lived in the Plymouth taverns, drinking the wondrous Plymouth ale, which was 'stronger than sack,' and cheap, and so full of alcohol that 'an halfe bowle' would make a sailor's wits like a merry-go-round. Plymouth at that time was full of wastrels and rogues. The chief clients of the ale-houses were runaway sailors, who, after entering for a voyage, and drawing an advance, or bounty, lay perdu till the ship had sailed. The society of the long-shore was highly undesirable. What with pirates and deserters and smugglers, at every street corner, honest John Ward had little incentive to be virtuous. By 1603 he had become a ragged, moody ruffian who got drunk every night 'with drinking of the King' among a company of 'scatter-goods and swaggerers.' He went by the name of Jack Ward, and had a reputation as a stout drinker and swearer. He used to sit on the tavern benches 'cursing the time' with a vehemence which won him the regard of all who heard. His biographer suggests that he paid no rent. The little money he possessed seems to have been spent in drink:

Ale was his eating and his drinking solely

so that 'all the day you should hardly faile but finde him in an ale-house: but bee sure to have him drunke at home at night.'

After a few months in Plymouth, his money (his savings, or the proceeds of the ketch) was exhausted. Plymouth ale became no longer feasible, nor would the hosts give him credit, and at this time he seems to have obtained some employment in one of the King's ships. It was not then a difficult business to enter a King's ship, and no doubt Ward had a wide acquaintance among the warrant officers of the ships in harbour. A word from one of them would have been sufficient to obtain a post for him. We do not know the exact nature of his employment, but it was probably that of ship-keeper, or petty-officer. As such, he went aboard the *Lion's Whelp*, a small man-of-war, then lying in the harbour. The work, whatever it was, was probably not very hard, nor does it appear that the ship had her full complement 'of 63 hands' aboard her. Ward helped to fit her for the sea, and made one of the crew (probably a scratch crew) which worked her round, shortly afterwards, to Portsmouth, where she anchored.

The Navy, at that time, was by no means a popular service. Sir Walter Raleigh, writing in this very year, tells us that 'They go with as great grudging to serve in his Majesty's ships as if it were to be slaves in the galleys.' Five years after this date, when matters had grown rather worse, under a Stuart administration, the Navy was 'for the greatest part manned with aged, impotent, vagrant, lewd and disorderly companions'; it had 'become a ragged regiment of common rogues.' Aboard the *Lion's Whelp* they were mostly old rovers who had sailed in the piratical raids of the last reign. The work they had to do while they lay in Portsmouth was not enough to keep them employed; and besides too much spare time, they had many causes for complaint.

It happened that Ward somehow came to hear of a recusant, a Roman Catholic gentleman, who was preparing to leave England for France, in order to enjoy 'liberty of conscience.' He had sold his estate near Petersfield, and had chartered a bark of twenty-five tons, to convey him to Havre. The bark lay at Portsmouth, not far from the *Lion's Whelp*, and aboard her (so Ward was informed) was the recusant's money. The religious issue probably did not weigh with Ward; but the thought of £2,000, 'in ready chinkes,' besides plate and jewels, was too much for him. His informant (no doubt one of the crew of the bark) may have exaggerated matters; but even with a considerable discount the bark must have seemed a most noble 'purchase.' Ward hastened to tell his brother warrants of the 'comfortable little dew of Heaven' lying so close beside them. They agreed with him that such an opportunity ought not to be allowed to pass. They had had enough of the King's service to last them through their lives, and there, in the little bark, was 'present pay' enough to keep them in affluence. They planned to go ashore together till the evening, when they would lay the bark aboard, make a prize of her, and carry her away to sea, there to rove as pirates 'to seek their desperate fortunes.'

The work they had to do aboard the *Lion's Whelp* was, as we have said, not enough to keep them busy. They had no difficulty in obtaining leave to go ashore, on the rather curious pretext that the steward did not give them a full allowance, and that they were hungry, and wished to buy themselves a square meal, at one of the inns by the Point. They went ashore together in one of the boats, and soon found a tavern to their taste. Here they sat down to disport themselves 'after the manner of sailors,' with the 'humming ale' and 'virtuous sacke' of their heart's desires. Very presently, although it was early in the day, they became drunk. They began to 'swagger,' or bluster, and in their songs and oaths, and drunken talk, they seem to have let fall a few dark hints of their intentions towards the recusant. The recusant happened to be ashore in Portsmouth waiting for the tide, or buying necessaries. He saw 'a ragged regiment of common rogues' rolling from inn to inn. He heard their oaths and menaces (or heard of them from some one he could trust), and became suspicious. Portsmouth was but a little town, and the presence of a drunken gang, at such a time, was disquieting. The recusant resolved to run no risks. He went aboard the little bark and conveyed ashore his 'ready chinkes,' with all his plate and jewels.

When the light began to fail, Ward's company took their boat and rowed to the bark. They laid her aboard very quietly, and carried her without opposition, for there were only 'two poor sneaks' in charge of her. They thrust this couple below, while some of them hove up the anchor, and got sail upon her. In a few minutes they were under way. They ran out to sea with a shout to the battery, and shaped a course to the westward.

It did not take the pirates many minutes to discover that they had been duped, and that the gold they had risked their necks for was not aboard. It took them sadly aback, and caused them 'to be ranck mad,' for there was no returning to Portsmouth. It was one of those awkward situations in which the great man gets an opportunity to explain himself. It was Ward's opportunity; and he rose to it at once. The recusant had provisioned the ship for the voyage with a profusion which did him honour. Although he had taken his money-bags, his 'nest of goldfinches,' he had not removed his 'turkey-pies,' his 'venison pasties,' and his 'sundry sorts of sacke'; so that there was no question of the pirates running short of food for some little time. Ward set a watch, and placed a good man at the helm, and called a council round his supper-table. They made a very excellent supper, and washed it down with what some one has called 'the learned poet's good.' As they ate and drank, they debated that if they ventured again into Portsmouth they would very speedily be hanged, at low water mark, as a warning to sailors. It was not very probable that they would be pursued; so that there was no immediate danger, and Ward proposed that they should cruise for a day or two off the Land's End; and then, if they met with any luck, put into Plymouth, to take off some of the men who had been his boon-companions there, before he joined the Navy. After that, he thought, they could 'commence pirates' on a more ambitious scale.

They could enter the Mediterranean, and join issue with the pirates of Algiers.

This project won the hearts of all present; so westward they sailed. In a day or two they had reached their cruising ground, near the Scilly Islands, and there they sighted a fine French merchantman, bound for Ireland. Ward sent his men below, so that the merchants should not suspect him. He ran up to the Frenchman and hailed him, in all friendship. The Frenchman suspected nothing; and for some time the two ships kept company. Presently, when Ward thought that the Frenchmen would be quite off their guards, he edged his bark alongside, and called his gang to board her. The surprise was complete. The Frenchmen were beaten down below, or flung overboard, and Ward found himself in possession of a ship of seventy tons, well-equipped, and armed. After this, he sailed for Plymouth, where he anchored in Cawsand Bay. Some of his company contrived to enter the town, where they persuaded a number of ruffians to leave the taverns and to come for a cruise. With these recruits, Ward thought himself strong enough to put to sea as a rover. He left Cawsand Bay and sailed away down Channel to the Spanish coasts.

He seems to have cruised for several months off the coast of Spain, with considerable success. He took a ship of one hundred tons, and a smaller vessel, a coaster, of the kind known as a sattee. In both these vessels he found recruits, besides gold and merchandise; so that, by the spring of 1604, he felt himself strong enough to proceed to Algiers, to league himself, as many English pirates had done before him, to the Algerine pirates, the scourges of the Mediterranean. But it chanced that, only a few weeks before he came to Algiers, one Richard Gifford, a pirate of renown, in the service of the Duke of Tuscany, had burnt some Algerine galleys, and killed many of the pirates on board them. The Algerines were retaliating by barbarous reprisals upon English merchantmen, and when Ward arrived off their city he found them particularly bitter. They refused his proffered alliance, and drove him from their ports. He therefore proceeded to Tunis, where he became a Turk (in order to satisfy the religious scruples of the natives), and made some satisfactory arrangement with the Bey, or Governor, a man named Osmund, or 'Crossyman.' In consideration of some large percentage of his profits this Bey, or 'Crossyman,' agreed to allow him to shelter and recruit at Tunis, and to use that port as a base from which he might sally out to rob at pleasure. The name Crossyman seems to be a corruption of Cara Osman, or Osman the Dark. Osman, it seems, had started life as a tailor.

It is difficult for one accustomed to the law and order of the present day to understand the dangers which threatened the Jacobean traveller. The seas swarmed with pirates; so that few merchantmen dared put to sea without arms; while very few came home without some tale of an encounter. There were pirates in the Atlantic, to intercept the ships coming home from the Newfoundland fisheries. There were pirates in the West Indies, roving for Spanish treasure-ships. There were pirates in the Orkneys, preying upon the Iceland trades. There were pirates near Ireland, especially in the south and the west, ranging over the Channel, and round these coasts. But there were, perhaps, more pirates in the Mediterranean than in all the other waters put together. In the Mediterranean they had the most part of the trade of Europe for their quarry; while the coasts of Africa, and the islands of the Archipelago, provided obscure harbours (with compliant Governors) for the recruiting of the companies after a cruise. The pirates, like the buccaneers a century later, preferred to cruise in small ships, in order that they might be less conspicuous and less likely to arouse the suspicion of the merchantmen. It was their custom to cruise in the swiftest ships they could find; and it must be remembered that their vessels, being small, could be propelled by sweeps when the wind failed them. When they sighted a ship which seemed to them to be a profitable quarry they contrived to follow her, without arousing her suspicions, until the evening, when they used to lay her aboard. If the quarry were slower than the cruiser, as generally happened, the pirates did not shorten sail, lest the merchants should suspect them. They carried their canvas as before, but they took care to slacken their progress by dragging a sea-anchor, a cask or two of water 'or other such like,' in the sea astern of them. They kept the sea in the very worst of weather 'by reason of the handiness of their ships and their skill as mariners.' It was their custom to take from their prizes not only the valuables such as gold and jewels, but the sea-stores, such as ropes, spars, sweeps, sails, and ship's provisions. With these 'recruits,' or 'plenishings,' they were able to keep out of harbour for many months at a time; and constant service made them excellent sailors. Their profits were enormous, and the risks they ran were not very great. The English Government, with its decayed Navy, could do very little against them. Spain was at war with Holland, and could not in any case spare ships from her West Indian convoys. Venice alone could trouble them; but the Venetian galleys, the only ships they dreaded, were expensive to the Venetian state, and by no means perfect as protectors of commerce. On the whole, the lot of the pirate was happy and free from care. To such a lot did John Ward devote himself, in the spring of 1604, after his relations with the Bey of Tunis had been established on what is known as 'a sound financial basis.' In a very few years he had made himself famous beyond expectation.

It seems that Ward prospered as a pirate from the time
of his first establishment at Tunis. He took a rich Venetian
'argosy' in his first cruise off the south of Spain, and a day
or two later he took a smaller ship, which he retained as his
flagship. He fitted her with four and twenty cannon, and
named her 'the Little John' after the comrade of Robin
Hood. Other pirates, among them a man named Simon
Dansekar, offered to form an alliance with him; and with
their forces, added to his own, he was strong enough for
'bold attempts.' He had at least four 'well-appointed'
ships under his command, with 'above two hundred
Englishmen, good soldiers, and expert mariners,' besides
Turks, to man them. With this squadron he took a huge
Venetian carrack, after a fierce fight. The carrack was the
Soderina; a wealthy merchantman, worth, it was said, some
half a million crowns. The credit of the capture was due to
Ward. The ship was gallantly defended, and would not
have been taken had not Ward driven his hands aboard
her at the point of his dagger. The wealth was safely
landed at Tunis, where it purchased Ward an abundant
popularity.

While dividing the spoils of this carrack, Ward quarrelled with his partner, Simon Dansekar. Dansekar, or
'Dansekar the Dutchman,' was a Fleming of Flushing,
who commenced pirate by running away with a ship from
Marseilles. He seems to have been a more humane man
than Ward; for he objected to Ward's habit of selling
Christian prisoners to the Turks. He was merciful to
merchants of his own nationality, while Ward robbed all
nations. When he quarrelled with Ward, he abandoned
Tunis, and removed his ships and pirates to Algiers. This
breaking-up of the partnership so weakened Ward's position with the Bey, that he seems to have been anxious for
his safety, and eager to make new alliances. An English
merchant, who saw him at Tunis at this crisis, writes of

him as being 'in a desperate plight,' eager to give up some 40,000 crowns' worth of booty, if, for such a bribe, King James would pardon him, and allow him to land in England, with some three hundred of his gang. However, the desperate plight was not so desperate as the merchant thought. According to Sir Henry Wotton, Ward was 'beyond a doubt the greatest scoundrel that ever sailed from England.' At the time of his application to King James he was preparing the *Soderina* for a piratical cruise 'with forty bronze pieces on the lower, and twenty on the upper deck.' He was also planning to obtain a 'letter of marque' from any Italian prince who would receive him, in the event of his failure to appease King James. It would appear that the application to King James was made through some courtier for a consideration. It was refused, because the Venetian ambassador, Zorzi Giustinian, demanded that no such pardon should be granted until the State of Venice, and all Venetian subjects, had been amply indemnified for their losses.

Zorzi Giustinian was able to trouble Ward in another way. At Tunis, the pirates' harbour, there was little market for merchandise. Ward had taken a great spoil of silk and indigo in the *Soderina*, but he could not dispose of it to his satisfaction among the Turks and Moors. He induced an English ship, which had put into Tunis for water, to take a lading of these goods, to dispose of them in Flanders. The Venetian Senate was admirably served by its spies. Giustinian received particulars of this ship, and induced the Lord High Admiral of England to watch for her. At the end of 1605, she was taken in the Channel, and carried into an English port. Her name was the *Husband*, and she was owned by London merchants. In her hold was some £10,000 worth of the *Soderina*'s cargo. Before this booty had been fully discharged, another ship, the *Seraphim*, arrived from Tunis with a similar freight. She, too, was arrested, and her cargo, or as much of it as could be proved to be Venetian, was handed back to Giustinian. Ward made one or two more attempts to open up a market in Europe, but the ships were taken, one after another, at Bristol and elsewhere, so that at last he abandoned the scheme. He waited at Tunis for several months for King James's answer to his request for pardon. When the royal refusal reached him, he put to sea again, partly to make more money to offer in bribes and partly to make the merchants more eager for him to be pardoned. At about this time, March 1606, a Royal Proclamation was issued for his suppression.

The cruise of 1608 was an eventful cruise for Ward. He had fitted out the *Soderina* for a flagship, and had mounted her with sixty or seventy brass guns. He had, besides, two smaller ships of war, both 'heavily manned and armed.' Altogether he seems to have commanded about four hundred men, three-fourths of whom were Turks or Moors, the others being Flemings, French, and Englishmen. One of the three ships foundered off Carthage early in the cruise. The other two roved up and down, and took two valuable Marseilles carracks.

While at sea, in his flagship, Ward lived in great state, with a double cabin guard of twelve Turks armed with scimitars. He had his 'music' (an English trumpeter), to play to him; and no doubt his cabin was sweet with many perfumes, and nobly furnished. In different parts of his ship were refreshment bars or canteens for the sale of wines and spirits. All his sailors received a daily allowance of strong drink; but if they wanted more they had to purchase it at one of these canteens. Sailors generally want more; and we read with small surprise that the discipline of the *Soderina* was not particularly good. The only law which has come down to us from her code is one forbidding, or at least discouraging, murder.

The piratical squadron turned eastward at the end of February 1608 bound to plunder 'the shipping of Syria.' Early in March, it came on to blow and the squadron was scattered. The great *Soderina*, with her frame much weakened by her numerous new gun-ports, and her upper works much strained by the weight of her new brass guns, began to labour and leak. 'About one hundred miles off Cerigo,' when the weather was at its worst, she started a plank, and went to the bottom. More than three hundred Turks sank with her. The sole survivors were 'four men and a boy' who were found afloat on some wreckage by a passing ship, going for Marseilles. Ward escaped with his life, owing to his skill as a boatman; for while the storm was at its worst he left the *Soderina* in a boat, in which he managed to get aboard the *Little John*. The news of the disaster reached Tunis before him through the five survivors who had been taken to Marseilles. When Ward returned there, after his cruise, he 'was nearly torn in pieces by the Janissaries,' who were furious with him for his desertion of the flagship, and for the loss of so many true believers. It cost Ward a large portion of his treasure to regain the confidence of his allies.

Shortly after the loss of the *Soderina*, an Englishman of the name of Pepwell, in the service of the English Lord Admiral, went to Tunis to convert Ward to a better habit of life. He failed to move that stony heart, as he failed, directly afterwards, in a plot to poison him. While he reasoned with, or tried to poison, Ward, that worthy's seamen were not idle. 'They so won his (Pepwell's) sailors that they became pirates,' leaving Pepwell to come home as best he might. There were several pirates lying at Tunis, all of them subordinate to Ward, and Pepwell at last won one of them, a Captain Bishop, to give him a passage to Venice. At Venice he gave Sir Henry Wotton, the English Ambassador, a minute account of Ward. He describes him as being 'about fifty-five years of age. Very short, with little hair, and that quite white; bald in front; swarthy face and beard. Speaks little, and almost always swearing. Drunk from morn till night. Most prodigal and plucky. Sleeps a great deal, and often on board when in ports. The habits of a thorough "salt." A fool and an idiot out of his trade.'

During the next few years, in spite of various losses, Ward seems to have prospered. It is said that he made a cruise to Ireland, with seven hundred men, and that he offered King James £40,000 for a pardon, which was refused. When he heard that his offer had been unavailing, he determined to settle down at Tunis. His old friend 'Crossyman,' gave him the remains of a castle, which he repaired with marble and alabaster, till it was 'a very stately house far more fit for a prince than a pirate.' He lived there, when not at sea, 'in a most princely and magnificent state. His apparel both curious and costly, his diet sumptuous.' He had two cooks to dress and prepare his diet for him, 'and his taster before he eats.' 'I do not knowe any peere in England,' says his biographer, 'that bears up his post in more dignity.'

It is not known how and when he died. Dansekar, his old ally, obtained a pardon from Henri IV of France, and entered the service of the Duke of Guise. Ward, as far as we can learn, was never pardoned. 'He lived there, in Tunis,' in his marble palace, where William Lithgow, the traveller, had supper with him, in the year 1615. Some say that Ward was drowned off Crete, and others that the Turks poisoned him. Both accounts are highly probable. It may be that, in his old age, he bought a pardon from a needy statesman, and settled down to die in Plymouth, where the ale was so good, and the company so congenial. He shares with Bartholomew Roberts the throne of English piracy. Those two alone, of the many who were called to the profession, practised it ever with a certain style, with some pretensions to the grand manner.

There is much literature concerning Ward. There are several ballads, of varying merit, describing an imaginary fight between his cruiser and a ship called the *Rainbow*, a King's ship sent to capture him. As Professor Laughton has pointed out, the real *Rainbow* never fought with Ward. Perhaps the name Rainbow is a corruption or popular version of *Tramontana*, the name of a small cruiser, which may once have chased him in the Irish Channel. In addition to the ballads, there is a play called 'A Christian turn'd Turk,' by the poet Robert Daborne. The play treats of Ward and his associates. It is based upon two chap-books concerning him; the one called 'Newes from Sea' (dated 1609), the other (far superior) by Andrew Barker, called 'A True and Certaine Report,' first published in the same year. There are numerous contemporary references to him. The best known is that in Ben Jonson's 'Alchemist,' act v, scene 2. There are others in Howell's Letters; in a play by Dekker ('If it be not a good Play'), in Donne's 15th Elegy, and in the 'Observations of Captain John Smith.' More trustworthy authorities concerning him are in the Venetian Series of State Papers, 1603–10; and in the Irish Series of State Papers, 1608–08. It may be added that the Sieur de Brèves, a French Ambassador, gives Ward, or 'Wer,' the credit of having taught the Moorish pirates to cruise in sailing-ships. Until his coming they relied on their galleys, which were excellent, but severely limited in their application to the art of piracy.

CAPTAIN JOHN JENNINGS[1]

It is not known where John Jennings was born; but it was almost certainly near the sea; and perhaps we should not be far wrong in saying that his parents were fisher folk, living on the South Coast. He was born, certainly, of poor parents; for his nameless biographer tells us that 'his education was so meane and low, he could neither write nor read.' The date of his birth does not appear, but

[1] The authorities for the life of Captain John Jennings are: (1) A chapbook of 'The Lives, Apprehensions, Arraignments and Executions of the 19 late Pyrates, namely, Capt. Harris, Jennings, Longcastle, Downes, Haulsey, and their companions, as they were severally indited on St Margret's Hill, in Southwark, on the 22 of December last and executed the Friday following. London. Printed for John Busby the Elder (1609); 4to.; black letter; 30 pp.' This document is very brightly and freshly written and generally accurate in that part of it which relates to our hero. (2) The documents in the Record Office (Cal. S. P. Dom. 1603–10; S. P. Venetian, 1607–10, and (especially) Irish Series, 1608–10).

An entry in the Stationers' Register mentions a poem by Jennings. The entry runs:

19no Marcij [1610–1]
Richard Jones Entred for his Copyes,
> Captayne Jenninges his songe, whiche he made in the Marshalsey and songe a little before his death. Item the second parte of the 'George Aloo' and the 'Swiftestake' (Sweepstake) beinge both ballades.

Both poems appear to have perished. The first part of the second ballad, 'The George Aloe (of Looe) and the Sweepstake, too' (quoted in 'Two Noble Kinsmen'), may be seen in Professor Child's 'English and Scottish Popular Ballads,' vol. v, p. 133, 4, 5.

possibly 1570, or a few years earlier, would be near the truth. He grew up 'wholly addicted to martial courses, and especially in the manly resolution of sea-faring men.' When he was a boy he shipped himself to sea, to scrub the cans in the galley, to say his compass to the boatswain, and to be whipped at the capstan every Monday morning, so that his ship might have a fair wind. When he grew older, he took his share in the work aloft, and learned how to point and parcel, how to hold his own in a forecastle, and how to load and fire a great gun. 'I grew,' he says, 'to beare the name of a skilful marriner. . . . I grew ambitious straight, to have a whole command, and held it baseness to live under checke.' He 'likt well,' he says, 'to see a captain give an order, and be obeyed on the instant.' He also 'likt well' to riot ashore, with good Plymouth ale, and other carnal matters, not obtainable by the foremast hand, when at sea.

As he saw no chance of rising to a command in the Navy or in the merchant service, he resolved to command independently. In some seaport he gathered a 'retchless crue' of rioters together; led them to the cutting out of a ship in the harbour, and ran away with her to sea. This was in the last years of the reign of Queen Elizabeth, at a time when the King of Spain was at war with Holland. Jennings' first move was to make for himself 'a safe refuge and retirement' in Dunkirk; probably by a money payment to the governor; and then having obtained a base, where he could revictual and careen, he began to play the pirate and to scour the Channel. He did not attack the English; but like John Ward, his great contemporary, he found his account in

> The jovial Dutchman
> As he met on the main.

It is possible that at this time he was a Roman Catholic, and that he omitted to attack the French and Spanish ships on religious grounds. However, there could have been few Spanish ships either safe to attack or worth attacking so far to the north; and no doubt the 'Dutch fly-boats, pinks, and passengers' brought his gang enough good spoils; both of 'ready chinkes' and provender. He soon became notorious. The Dutch complained to the English government; and ships were sent to cruise for him. His own ship, like most pirate ships, was chosen from many prizes for her speed. By his ship's speed and his own vigilance he escaped the cruisers for a long time; but at last, through too much aqua-vitæ, or an unlucky shot, he was caught, and carried to England, where he was lodged in the Marshalsea in irons, to wait for the next gaol delivery. His ship was either restored to her owners or sold to cover expenses. The terror of the Channel was now a plucked crow in a cage, with nothing to expect but a hempen cord, and present death at Wapping Stairs.

His sister heard of his arrest, and at once began to petition the merchants he had robbed, that they should not press their suits. Her brother, she told them, was a man who might be of the greatest service to them; he was a reformed character, who had pledged his honour to live virtuously in the future; he was a man of whom any country might be proud; and much more to the same tune. Was this a man to send to the gallows? Why? It was 'proudly spoken' of Captain Jennings, 'that not a man in Christendom could stop a leak under water better than he'; if 'without boasting' (as he himself says), 'so wel' as he. It was true that he had been a little fresh or so; but then the sea air, and youth, were great provocatives; and it was, after all, by men like Jennings that our imperial destiny was maintained. By blarney of this kind, and by suggesting that the courage and energy of their prisoner might really do them good service, the girl persuaded the merchants to petition the Queen for the life of him who had robbed them. Jennings was pardoned for his two worst offences; his prison charges were paid; and one of the Holland merchants (who perhaps feared a relapse) gave him the command of a fine fly-boat, and sent him to sea to carry wool and wine.

He did not succeed as a sea-captain. Aboard that Holland fly-boat there was 'barratry of the master and mate,' if nothing worse, so that she did not pay for her tar and tallow. The pay of a sea-captain was small, and the proud heart of Jennings did not like the reproofs of his employers. The fly-boat was strongly built, and no doubt carried half-a-dozen quick-firing guns. Jennings waited for a good opportunity, corrupted the hearts of his sailors, and then ran away with ship, crew, and furniture, to try the fortune of the sea once more, 'on the bonny coasts of Barbary.' As he steered south, he sighted a Spanish caravel. He fired his little guns into her, laid her aboard, and made her his prize. Then he sailed on again, till he reached the Barbary coast.

As soon as he arrived at Safi he was seized by the Dey and flung into prison; where he found other English pirates, waiting for the bowstring or the galleys, to tell him the reason for this harsh reception. The pirates had agreed with the Dey, it seems, on the half-share system. The Dey supplied hands, stores, a fortified base, and good careenage; the pirates gave in return one-half of all their spoils, either slaves or goods, at the end of each cruise. The pirates had broken their contracts, and the Dey had therefore imprisoned them; sending Jennings with the rest to deter him from a similar lapse in time to come. He stayed in prison till he had paid to the Dey a large share of his Spanish prize. Then he was released, with permission to fit his fly-boat for the sea.

We cannot date his coming to Safi; but it must have been a few years after the accession of James I. England was then at peace with the world. There was no 'flourishing employment' for seamen. Those 'haughty hearts' who had been with Drake at Cartagena, with Newport at Truxillo, or with Essex at Fayal, picking up 'a few crowns, a few reasonable booties' had now 'to picke up crums at a lowe ebb'; and to vail their sea-bonnets to 'such as pearkt up their heads to authority in this time of quiet.' There was nothing stirring against Spain. Such men-of-war as were commissioned, were manned by vagrants and thieves, who deserted when they could. In these circumstances, any sailor who had seen the 'daies of bickering,' and had a passion for glory in him, was strongly tempted to turn pirate. A very great number of them did so. During the first years of the reign of James I the seamen who had made Elizabeth's Navy what it was, brought their skill and craft to the making of a pirate navy, which can only be compared to the buccaneer fleets of Morgan, Mansvelt, Sawkins, and Edward Davis, some seventy years later. From the crook of the Algerine mole, and from the sharp gut of the Goletta, these English seamen sailed out against the merchants of Spain and Italy. They were a ruinous hindrance to all Mediterranean traders. Their spoils were enormous; and they were able to live in luxury and riot.

In the Channel, they made their bases among the creeks and bays of South-western Ireland, notably in Dingle Bay and Bantry Bay, where there are sheltering islands, to hide them from any wandering cruiser. They had little to fear as a rule; for the cruiser always on the coast was a small, ill-manned ship of 200 tons, which could only keep the seas during the summer months. The pirate ships were generally better found than the King's ships; and, as they were kept clean by frequent careening, they had the heels of them if it came to a chase. 'The English are good sailors,' said one who knew, 'but they are better pirates.' Before Jennings fell, an organized fleet of pirates kept the south coast of Ireland in a state of siege, for weeks at a time. They were disciplined like a fleet of King's ships, and so powerful that they could land 300 men at any point, at short notice. The business which Jennings followed was at least carried on in some style.

While he lay at Safi, some allies of John Ward, two Tunisian pirates, named Bishop and Roope, put in there for wood and water. Jennings made a compact with them, and accompanied them on a roving cruise, in which they took a huge booty, to spend in riot ashore. Bishop quarrelled with his partners during their stay ashore: so that Roope and Jennings sailed without him, when they next put to sea. Roope's ship sprang a leak during the cruise, so he and his seamen came aboard Captain Jennings'. They took a Spanish fly-boat, and sent her north, in the care of some pirates, for sale in Dunkirk, but she was captured by an English man-of-war.

After this capture, the allies sailed into the Channel, and snapped up some French wine ships off the Isle of Wight. Off the Land's End, they took a ship of Bristol, with a valuable general cargo, which they transhipped. Off the Scilly Islands they took a French ship 'laden with brasse, and other rich commodities'; and then they ran short of provisions, and bore up for Baltimore. At Baltimore they sent in the purser 'to deale with the Kernes for hogges to victuall withal.' They had a tender with them, a small Spanish caravel, a lately taken prize, when they appeared off the town, so that the Baltimore authorities, seeing the ships in company, could have had no doubt of what they were. Jennings realized that the authorities might not care to sell their hogs to people of his way of life. In the long-boat which bore the purser, he sent 'a token of familiaritie' to the governor of the town; the said token being '19 or 20 chests of sugers' and 4 chests of fine scarlet coral. For this bountiful bribe they received permission to wood, water and reprovision; and also, it seems, to sell some of their spoils to the citizens. While he lay at Baltimore, Jennings 'fell in liking with an Irish woman' whom he carried with him to sea, in spite of the growlings of his men, who swore that the compass would never traverse right, nor a fair wind blow with a female living aft. It was all through her, they said, that they met the King's cruiser as they left Baltimore Road; and it was all through her that they had to cut and run for it, instead of making her a prize. A few days later, they had another stroke of bad luck, undoubtedly due to the presence of a female aboard. They attacked two Spanish ships who fought them courageously and gave them a battering. Ten good men were killed and more than twenty badly hit, Jennings himself being one of the wounded.

> At the end of a watch, of a watch so severe
> There was scarcely a man left was able for to steer,
> There was scarcely a man left could fire off a gun,
> And the blood down the deck like a river it did run.

Jennings had to sheer off in distress under such sail as he could carry and be thankful that the Spaniards did not give chase. The seamen made some repairs, and then held a fo'c's'le council about the Irish woman in the cabin. 'See what comes,' they said, 'of carrying women to sea.' They agreed in the end that their defeat was 'a just judgment of God against them'; not for any little robberies or murders which they had done, but for 'suffering their captaine . . . to wallow in his luxuries.' Why should he have his luxury any more than the rest of the crew? Captain Roope was insistent with this question till the crew swore that they would put an end to these Babylonish practices once for all. 'In a giddy manner,' they broke into the captain's cabin, and 'boldly began to reprove his conduct.' Wounded as he was, John Jennings started from his cot, seized 'a trunchion,' or handy belaying pin, and banged about him till he had 'beaten them all to a bay.' As he got his breath, they rushed in upon him a second time, and drove him aft into the gun-room. He bolted the door against them; but they fired on him through the key-hole. Then Captain Roope quieted the mutineers, set a guard at the gun-room door, and took command of the ship.

He was 'a man of more stern and obdurate nature than Jennings was.' He hazed his hands with unnecessary work till they longed for the old order, with good Babylonish Jennings in command. They released their old captain; and as soon as they had taken another ship, they put Captain Roope from command, and restored Jennings to his doxy and his quarterdeck.

The taking of this new ship was a serious matter. She was a richly-laden Amsterdam ship, of 180 tons, manned by French and Dutch sailors. She fought valiantly, for several hours, costing the pirates a sore mauling and the loss of sixty men killed and wounded. Jennings had been shaken by his wound, and by the late mutiny. His ship was battered and broken. He was short of men and provisions; his decks were full of wounded; and 'he desired now in heart he might make his peace . . . although with the tender of all he had.' His first step was to put in at Baltimore, where he hoped to submit himself to the Lord Clanricarde, and to obtain refreshments. When he came to Baltimore, he sent in his boat with another present to buy him a fair reception, but his boat's crew deserted, without making any overtures, and Jennings, fearing that his men had been arrested, put to sea at once, intending to sail to the Shannon, to try the Earl of Thomond.

On his way to the Shannon, he called at various ports to get refreshments. His men rummaged through most of the towns on the coast, 'and impeacht even their ordinary trade,' though Lord Danvers did his best to stop them by ordering all provisions to be carried far inland. In the middle of January 1609, the two ships anchored in the Shannon, not far from Limerick, in the country of the Earl of Thomond, to whom the pirates wrote the following letter:

RIGHT HONOURABLE, we beseech your Lordship to suffer us so far to imboulden ourselves upon your lordship's favour, as to be our mediator unto our Lord Deputy, for ye pardoning of our offences, assuring your Lordship that we never offended any of the King's subjects. If your L will undertake the obtaining of our pardon, we will deliver over, unto my L deputy and your L the ship that we have now, with such lading and commodities, as we have hereunder written; further desiring your L in regard of the foulness of the weather, besides the eating up of my vitles that we may hear from the Lord deputy within this 14 dayes, for longer we may not stay; for ye country upon your L command will not relieve us with any victuals. Theis are the parcels and commodities.

20 peces of ordnance, saker and minion (5 pr and 4 pr M L guns).
7 murtherers (small B L guns of a mortar type, firing dice shot).
40 chests of sugars.
4 bags of pepper.
12 ? and chists of sinamond.
4 bags of Spanish woll.
1 barrell of waxe & a boykett.
4 chists of soap.
1 canne of brasse, with cabells, anchers & all necessaries fitting a ship of her burthen, being 300 tons; all wh shall be delivered if it please ye L deputie; I onlie desire a general pardon my self, and these men, whose names shall be written underneath; with a

passe for all my companie to travell where it please
them, for the wh we shall wish all increase of happi-
ness to yr L from ye River of Shanon this 23 of Jan.
1608.

Your L (word *servants* erased in another ink) to
commaunde

> JOHN JENINGES
> KIDWELL ALS CADWALLADER TREVOR
> GILB ROOPE
> PETER JACOBSON.

The Earl of Thomond received this letter, and weighed it
carefully. By means of spies 'he discerned a disposition'
among some of the pirates 'even to enterprise upon their
fellows.' He wished to enter into no composition with such
a man as Jennings if other means could be found to bring
him in. He therefore temporized; sent his sons aboard to
see the pirate ships, and allowed them to take costly gifts
from their captains. One of his spies offered to take
Jennings single handed; but for this bold deed the spy
demanded the whole of Jennings' booty. The Earl gave
him no encouragement but told him he might try, if he
wished. Meanwhile he continued to sound Captain Roope
and others of the pirates, for signs of disaffection.

He did not feel himself strong enough to attack the
ships; but by March 1609, he had engaged four of the
pirates – Trevor, Roope, a man called Drake, and Peter
Jacobson, the sailing master – to deliver ship and goods to
his Majesty, when called upon. On the night of the 20th
March, he went aboard her with a guard. The traitors
handed over the ship, as they had promised, and though
Jennings, or some faithful hand, destroyed the Earl's right
arm, the struggle was soon over, and the sea-hawk was
safely caged in one of the Earl's gaols.

Jennings' ship was not worth very much. Most of her

men left her, and put to sea in the prize, directly her captain had been taken. The Earl overhauled her as soon as he could. He wrote how 'the Comodities aboard is butt ordinairie, and a lytell sugers wh is so blacke as yt is worth but lytell in this land.' She is very chargeable, he says, lying in the best road in the river. She could not be careened, as she was 'to weke,' and she was so much battered, she was really worthless. What became of her does not appear. Her guns, her chists of sinamond, and her solitary boykett were put ashore, and the rest of her was probably sold to the highest bidder, for firewood and building material. The Earl thought that her seamen carried off the best of the spoil in their 'great breeches.' His wound had kept him from watching them at the time of the capture; so the booty, setting aside Jennings, 'in his light doublet and hose,' was but paltry. As for Jennings, he was sent over to Chester, in July 1609; and from Chester, by easy stages, he came to London for trial, and lodged once more in the Marshalsea prison.

In the Marshalsea, he behaved himself with becoming courage. 'He lived a careless life,' says his biographer. 'One being merry drinking with him once, demanded of him,' how he had lived at sea? He replied that he had ever rejoiced more to hear the cannon than the sound of the church bell, and that he fought not 'as chickens fight,' for meat; 'but for store of gold, to maintain riot.' At another time, in hot weather, as he sat drinking with friends in the prison parlour, it was observed that he sat with his face in the sun, in contempt of headache. 'I shall hang in the sun, shortly,' he said, 'and then my neck will ache. I do but practise now.' Later, in the autumn, there was a fall of snow; so that he could cheer up his heart with a game at snowballs. Then his old friend Captain Harris, whom he had known in Barbary, was committed to the Marshalsea; to comfort him with fellowship and cups of sack. It was reported that the two were 'mad drunke' together; but that was calumny. They were only 'orderly merry' together; and they had now but little time either for merriment or for sorrow. At the trial, Jennings did his best to save two of his crew; who, as he told the Court, had been compelled to turn pirates at the pistol muzzle. 'Alas, my Lord,' he cried to the Judge, 'what would you have these poor men say . . . if anything they have done they were compelled unto it by me; 'tis I must answer for it.'

All three were condemned in spite of his pleading (Dec. 3rd, 1609); but five days later they obtained a respite; as the King hoped to obtain information from them, to help him in the extirpation of other pirates. It was not till the 22nd of December that they were led out to suffer. John Burles, the curate of St Bennet's, attended John Jennings. The others had their own priests, and as their irons were knocked off they raised their voices in the penitential psalms. Burles was much grieved for Jennings. 'A marvellous proper man,' he notes sadly. He might have been a hero, under a better King.

They were rowed to Wapping in wherries, to the sound of the rogue's march beaten on a drum. They looked their last on ships and river, glad, it would seem, to be at last free of them. It was a fine sunny morning; and the sailors on the ships at anchor bade them cheer up, as they rowed past. When they came to the Stairs, Jennings made a speech (there was a great crowd), bidding his two men to follow him as fearlessly as they had followed him of old, when the shot was flying. Some pirates on these occasions used to tear up their 'crimson taffety breeches,' to give the rags as keepsakes to those who stood by. No breeches were torn on this occasion. The dying men spoke briefly to the crowd, regretting their sins: then prayed for a few moments with their priests, and died cheerfully, singing psalms, one after the other, 'like good fellows.'

THE VOYAGE OF THE *CYGNET*

In the year 1683–4 some eminent London merchants, fired by the perusal of the buccaneer accounts of South America (the journals of Sharp, Ringrose, Cox, and others), conceived a scheme for opening up a trade with Peru and Chili. They subscribed among themselves a large sum for the equipment and lading of a ship. The Duke of York, then Lord Admiral, gave the project his princely patronage. A ship, the *Cygnet*, was chosen and fitted for the voyage, and a trusty master mariner, one esteemed by Henry Morgan, was appointed her captain. This was Charles Swan, or Swann, a man whose surname eminently fitted him for the command of a ship so christened. Following the custom of the time, two merchants, or supercargoes, took passage with Captain Swan to dispose of the lading, and to open up the trade. The *Cygnet* sailed from the Thames with a costly general cargo, which was designed not only to establish just relations with the Spanish-Americans, but to pay her owners from 50 to 75 per cent. As the voyage was not without interest we propose to consider some of its most striking events.

We are sorry to have to state that by October 1684, Captain Swan had become a buccaneer, and his ship, the *Cygnet*, the flagship of a small squadron cruising on the coast of Peru, against the subjects of the King of Spain, with whom we were then at peace. Swan had met with Captain Edward Davis, a buccaneer of fame, and the meeting had been too much for him. When the clay pot meets the iron pot there is usually a final ruin; and the meeting put an end to the dreams of a South American trade. 'There was much joy on all sides,' says the chronicler, writing of this meeting, but presumably the greater joy was Davis's, who gave Swan an immediate hint that the *Cygnet* was too deeply fraught to make a cruiser. 'Therefore (Captain Swan) by the consent of the supercargoes, got up all his goods on Deck, and sold to any *that would buy upon trust*: the rest was thrown overboard into the sea, except fine goods, as Silks, Muslins, Stockings, &c., and except the Iron.' The iron was saved for ballast. The other goods made very delicate wear for the fo'c's'le hands.

When all was ready, the allied forces sailed to take Guayaquil, but met with no luck there, through 'one of Captain Davis's men, who showed himself very forward to go to the town, and upbraided others with faintheartedness: yet afterwards confessed (that he) privately cut the string that the Guide was made fast with, (and) when he thought the Guide was got far enough from us, he cried out that the Pilot was gone, and that somebody had cut the Cord that tied him . . . and our consternation was great, being in the dark and among Woods'; so that 'the design was wholly dashed.' After this they sailed to the Bay of Panama, where they planned to lie at anchor to wait for the yearly treasure fleet from Lima. While they waited, Captain Swan sent a letter over the Isthmus, with a message to his employers.

March 4, 1685.

PANAMA ROAD.

CHARLES SWANN to Capt. JOHN WISE.

My voyage is at an end. In the Straits of Magellan I had nine men run from me in one night, after they saw that they could not prevail with me to play the rogue. But God's justice overtook them, for after weathering Cape Victory we met with an extreme storm of long continuance, which drove me down to lat 55° 30' S and in which the ship to which they deserted was lost. Then I came to Valdivia, when I had two men killed under a flag of truce, after three days' parley and all oaths human and divine. An ambuscade of between one and two hundred men came out, and fired upon a poor eight of us in the yawl. But God punished them likewise, as we hear, we killing three of their captains and some others. It is too long to give you an account of all my troubles, which were chiefly owing to the fact that the ship was meant to be run away with. In Nicoya the rest of my men left me, so that, having no one to sail the ship, I was forced to join them. So that now I am in hostility with the Spaniards, and have taken and burnt some towns, and have forced the President of Panama to send me two men he had taken from us. The same day 270 new men came to me, and we are going to take in 200 more that they left behind. We shall soon be 900 men in the South Seas. Assure my employers that I do all I can to preserve their interest, and that what I do now I could in no wise prevent. So desire them to do what they can with the King for me, for as soon as I can I shall deliver myself to the King's justice and I had rather die than live skulking like a vagabond for fear of death. The King might make this whole Kingdom of Peru tributary to him in two years' time. We now await the Spanish fleet that brings the money to Panama. We were resolved to fight them before we had reached this strength, and had lain in wait 6 months for them, but now we hear that they are at sea, and expect them every day. If we have success against them we shall make a desperate alarm all Europe over. I have some money which I wish were with you, for my wife. I shall, with God's help, do things which (were it with my Prince's leave) would make her a lady; but now I cannot tell but it may bring me to a halter. But if it doth my comfort is that I shall die for that I cannot help. Pray present my faithful love to my dear wife, and assure her she is never out of my mind.

After failing in his attempt upon the treasure fleet, Captain Davis, the Buccaneer Commodore, took his squadron towards Rio Lejo, on the western coast of Mexico, where, 'about 8 leagues from the shore,' at eight in the forenoon, 520 buccaneers, mostly English, went down the sides of their ships into their boats. There were thirty-one canoas for their accommodation, some of them of nearly forty feet in length, and five or six feet broad. They were 'dug-outs' of the most primitive type, but the buccaneers were not particular as to the build of their crafts. They settled upon their thwarts; one of them piped a song, 'and the rowers, sitting well in order,' began to plough the wine-dark sea.

At two in the afternoon, a squall beat down upon them. The sea rose with tropical swiftness, so that, in half an hour 'some of our Canoas were half full of water, yet kept two men constantly heaving it out.' They could do nothing but put right before the wind. 'The small Canoas,' it is true, 'being most light and buoyant, mounted nimbly over the surges, but the great heavy Canoas lay like Logs in the Sea, ready to be swallowed by every foaming Billow.' However, the danger did not last very long. The squall blew past, and, when the wind abated, the sea went down; so that by '7 a clock in the Evening, it was quite calm and the Sea as smooth as a Mill-pond.' They passed that night in the canoas five leagues from the shore, huddled anyhow, with cramped limbs. In the morning they stretched themselves, and lay by, till another squall set them pulling for the land, like the seamen in the temperance hymn. In the night of August 10 they entered Rio Lejo harbour, and slept peacefully in the shelter of the great red mangrove trees, which rose up 'plentiful and thick' from the very lip of the sea.

When day dawned they rowed up the Lejo river. A Spanish breastwork stood upon the river bank to guard the passage; but its garrison was composed of Nicaraguan Indians, a race 'very Melancholy and Thoughtful, and presently they ran away to give notice of our Approach.' The buccaneers were a little vexed at this example of the effect of melancholy, but did not allow it to depress them. They landed from their canoas, selected a boatguard of fifty of their most intelligent hands and drew up the remainder into battalia, according to the Art of War. 'Captain *Townley*, with eighty of the briskest Men marched before, Captain *Swan* with 100 Men marched next, Captain *Davis* with 170 Men marched next, and Captain Knight brought up the Rear.' Then, with many joyful anticipations, they took to the road, across 'a Champion Country, of long grassy Savannah, and spots of high Woods,' meaning to surprise the City of Leon.

The City of Leon had a great reputation among them; for, although it was of no great size, and 'of no great Trade, and therefore not rich in Money,' it had been praised in print, some thirty years before, by 'the English Mexican' Mr Thomas Gage. We read that it was 'very curiously built' on 'a sandy Soil, which soon drinks up all the Rain that falls.' It had a famous rope-walk, and a number of sugar-works, besides cattle farms and tallow boileries. The houses were of white stone roofed with a vivid red pantile, 'for the chief delight of the inhabitants consisteth in their houses, and in the pleasure of the Country adjoyning, and in the abundance of all things for the life of man, more than in any extraordinary riches, which there are not so much enjoyed as in other parts of *America*. They are contented with fine gardens, with variety of singing birds and parrets, with plenty of fish and flesh, which is cheap, and with gay houses, and so lead a delicious lasie and idle life. . . . And especially from the pleasure of this City is all that Province of Nicaragua, called by the Spaniards *Mahomet's* Paradise, the Paradise of *America*.'

At about 3 o'clock that afternoon, Captain Townley, 'only with his eighty Men,' marched into the square to taste 'the pleasure of this City.' There were 200 Spanish horse, and five companies of infantry drawn up to oppose him; but, as nearly always happened in these tussels, 'two or three of their Leaders being knock'd down, the rest fled.' Captain Townley marched in, and piled arms in the

Plaza. At decent intervals the other companies joined him; 'and Captain Knight with as many Men as he could incourage to march, came in about 6, but he left many Men tired on the road; these, as is usual, came dropping in one or two at a time, as they were able.' Among the tired men, 'was a stout old Grey-headed Man, aged about eighty-four, who had served under *Oliver* in the time of the Irish Rebellion . . . and had followed Privateering ever since.' He was 'a very merry hearty old Man, and always used to declare he would never take quarter'; so that, when the Spaniards surrounded him, as he sat resting by the roadside, he gaily 'discharged his Gun amongst them' keeping 'a Pistol still charged.' The Spaniards drew back and 'shot him dead at a distance.' His name was Swan.

Peace hath her victories, no less renowned than war. 'Mr Smith was tired also,' and Mr Smith was neatly lazoed, and dragged before the Spanish Governor before he was well awake. 'He being examined how many Men we were, said 1000 at the City, and 500 at the Canoas, which made well for us at the Canoas, who straggling about every day might easily have been destroyed.' Mr Smith dipped his pen in earthquake and eclipse till the Spanish Governor 'sent in a Flag of Truce,' in the hope of coming to a composition, and getting rid of such an army. The buccaneers received the Flag with all due ceremony, and demanded some £70,000 as a ransom for the town, with a further douceur of 'as much Provision as would victual 1000 Men four Months, and Mr Smith to be ransomed.' However, a ransom of such proportions was not readily forthcoming. The pirates waited patiently for a few days, pillaging 'all they could rob,' and then set fire to the place:

> And when the town burned all in flame
> With tara tantara away we all came.

75

The Spaniards 'sent in Mr Smith,' the next morning, 'and had a gentlewoman in exchange.' An impartial judge must admit that they had the better of the bargain.

Having destroyed the town of Leon, the buccaneers marched upon Rio Lejo, 'a pretty large town with three Churches' some two leagues from the harbour. It was a very sickly place, never free from a noisome smell, and had therefore 'an Hospital' with 'a fine Garden belonging to it.' The way thither was defended by a very strong re-doubt, yet their labour was but lost that built it, for 'we fired but two guns, and they all ran away.' Rio Lejo was rich in flour, 'Pitch, Tar and Cordage; These things we wanted, and therefore we sent them all aboard.' The pirates obtained also a 'purchase' of '150 Beefs,' and 'visited the Beef-Farm every day, *and* the Sugar Works, and brought away every Man his Load.' In spite of the noisome smell, they passed a pleasant week at Rio Lejo, 'and then some of our destructive Crew set fire to the Houses,' and 'we marched away and left them burning.' The army then returned to the ships. The next day the fleet divided, and Davis and Swan parted company. William Dampier, who tells us most of these things, left the service of Davis here, and joined his fortunes with Swan's. He had been Davis's navigator for some time and he filled some similar post under Swan, who had perhaps attracted him as a weak but cultivated man will attract the cultivated strong man who has no one else to talk with. Captain Swan lingered for some days more at the anchor-age, and then cruised slowly to the north, along the surf-beaten Western Coast. Captain Townley, the leader of the eighty brisk Men, remained as his vice-admiral.

The history of their cruise is a history of bold incom-petence. They landed, and fought, and fell ill, and sailed, and again landed; but they got very little save a knowledge of geography. When they came as far to the north as

Acapulco, it occurred to them that they were in season to take the annual galleon from Manila, a prize worth some half a million of our money, and the constant dream of every pirate in the Pacific. Cavendish had taken one such galleon a century before; and Rogers was to take another some thirty years later. When the *Cygnet* arrived near Acapulco the citizens were expecting her arrival. Had the buccaneers but filled their provision casks at once, and proceeded to a cruising station off Cape Corrientes, they could not have failed of meeting with her. Had they met her, they would probably have taken her. Had they taken her, they would have shared some £2,000 apiece, in addition to the merchandise. It was not to be. The brisk Captain Townley wasted some precious time trying to cut out a ship from Acapulco. Then some more precious time was wasted in collecting provisions at places where there was little to collect. By the time the *Cygnet* was ready to cruise for the galleon, that golden ark was safe in harbour, under the guns of a fort.

After a few more profitless adventures, Captain Townley parted company. Swan then proposed that the *Cygnet* should proceed to the East Indies to cruise 'off the Manila's.' He had no intention of 'cruising' there; but without a lure of the kind his men would never have consented; for 'some thought, such was their ignorance, that he would carry them out of the World; for about 2 thirds of our Men did not think there was any such Way to be found,' as the Way across the Pacific to Guahan and the Philippines, and even if there were a way, they did not know how long a passage they might have. Cavendish had made it in forty-four, and Drake in sixty-eight days, but the English books reckoned the distance to be but 6,000 miles, whereas all the Spanish 'waggoners' made it 7,000, or more. Even if it were but 6,000 miles they had scarcely enough food to carry them so far. 'We had not 60 days' provision, at a little more than half a pint of Maiz a day for each Man, and no other Provision, except three meals of salted *Jew-fish*; and we had a great many Rats aboard, which we could not hinder from eating part of our Maiz.' However, 'the hope of gain' worked 'its Way through all Difficulties.' The men tightened their belts and promised themselves a good dinner when they got ashore. The maize was divided between the *Cygnet* and a little bark, which was still cruising with her. At the end of March 1686, they took their departure from Cape Corrientes, and stood out into the unknown, towards dinnerless days, and what might come.

'In all this Voyage,' says Dampier, 'we did not see one Fish.'

Following Dampier's example, we shall not trouble the reader 'with an account of each day's run,' but hasten 'to the less known parts of the world.' The hungry buccaneers made Guahan on the 20th May. 'It was well for Captain Swan that we got sight of it before our Provisions was spent, of which we had but enough for three days more, for, as I was afterwards informed, the Men had contrived, first to kill Captain Swan and eat him when the Victuals was gone, and after him all of us who were accessary in promoting the undertaking this Voyage.' Captain Swan made a seasonable jape on the occasion of his hearing this. 'Ah, Dampier,' he said, 'you would have made them but a poor Meal,' for 'I' (explains Dampier) 'was as lean as the Captain was lusty and fleshy.'

At Guahan the pirates received a present of six Hogs, 'most excellent Meat,' the best that Dampier 'ever eat.' Having eaten them, they salted some fifty more, and 'steered away' for Mindanao, where they anchored on 18th July 1686.

When they arrived at Mindanao, most of the seamen had had enough of roving. They 'were almost tired, and began to desire a *quietus est*,' for they had had a long cruise, and Captain Swan by one means or another (possibly through Dampier), had given them a severe disciplining on the way. 'Indeed Captain Swan had his Men as much under Command as if he had been in a King's Ship.' It was now open to him to retrieve his credit by establishing a trade at Mindanao. He could easily have obtained cloves and nutmegs there in any quantity; for the Mindanayans were eager to make an alliance with the English, and would have given him 'good Pennyworths' for the £5,000 in gold which he had brought with him. He seems to have had some intention of establishing such a spice trade; but it came to nothing. His men made merry ashore 'with their Comrades and Pagallies,' and Captain Swan made bargains with the Raja, who fooled him to the top of his bent, and sponged upon him. By-and-by the crew became mutinous, 'all for want of action.' They took to selling the iron ballast for honey and arrack 'to make punch'; so that the ship was soon 'by the ears,' with all hands 'drunk and quarrelsome.' Then a young man came upon the Captain's private journal 'in which Captain Swan had inveighed bitterly against most of his Men.' This was enough to draw the mutiny to a head. The sailors were ready for anything. 'Most of them despaired of ever getting home and therefore did not care what they did, or whither they went.' It struck them that they would have less worry if they sailed elsewhere, leaving Captain Swan with his Raja. They got some of their drunken mates aboard, and so set sail, leaving Captain Swan, with thirty-six others, ashore at Mindanao. The Raja kept Captain Swan for a little while, and then caused him to be upset from a canoe into the river, and stabbed as he strove to swim ashore. That was the end of Captain Charles Swan.

As for the *Cygnet*, with the 'mad Crew,' she sailed from

island to island at the sweet will of the thirsty souls aboard her. She made a prolonged stay at one of the Batan group, 'which we called Bashee Island, from a Liquor which we drank there plentifully every day.' 'Indeed,' says Dampier, 'from the plenty of this Liquor, and their plentiful use of it, our Men called all these Islands the *Bashee* Islands.'

But even of Bashee there came satiety. After some weeks they determined that 'Bashee drink' was vanity; so they 'weigh'd from there,' and wandered as far as Australia, and then stood west for Sumatra. Presently they reached the Nicobar Islands, where Dampier and two others went ashore, having had enough of such shipmates. The *Cygnet*'s men made some demur at their landing; but at last agreed to let them go; so that on 'a fine clear Moon-light Night,' as the newly landed men were walking on the sands, they 'saw her under Sail,' going out upon some further madness. They watched her go, and thanked their stars that they were quit of her.

'This mad fickle Crew were upon new Projects again.' They were going to Persia, no less; but they never got there. They had to put in to the Coromandel coast for water, and here 'the main Body were for going into the Mogul's Service.' 'It was what these men had long been thinking and talking of as a fine Thing,' so now they put it into practice. They throve mightily in the Mogul's service; but they could not remain in it for very long. Most of them crept back to the coast, to ship themselves elsewhere, and some 'went up and down Plundering the Villages,' till the Mogul's hair was grey. Those who stayed by the *Cygnet* tried to take her to the Red Sea. On the way they took a rich Portuguese ship, which they gutted. Later on, some of the *Cygnet*'s men went off with a New York slaver; and at last the whole crew left her, in order to go to Achin, 'having heard there was plenty of Gold there.' Some sailors of another vessel 'undertook to carry her for England'; but she was old and rotten; and her days above sea were numbered. 'In St Augustin's Bay in Madagascar' her crew went ashore, having broken their hearts at her pumps ever since they joined her. In St Augustin's Bay she slowly filled to her port-sills, and at last sank gracefully, her little blue vane still fluttering, to puzzle the mermaids with her bales of silk stockings.

CAPTAIN ROBERT KNOX

Between the years 1690 and 1714, at odd times between voyages, two sea captains used to meet each other in London, dine together, shift their tides, and then go off again trading to the coast or hunting the never-caught galleon, as their marvellous fates led them. Both had endured more than man is usually given to endure, both had tasted to the full of life's unexpectedness; but perhaps the strangest of all the strange things that happened to them was this – that once or twice, before they met each other, their wanderings brought them close together and then swept them apart, as though life had determined that their two souls should never know each other in action, only meet when the action was done, to complete each other's sagas from complemental memories; Dampier to hear from Knox what happened to the *Cygnet*'s crew, Knox to hear from Dampier how that crew came into being.

We have no record of any of the conversations between them; but it is plain that sometimes (when they got away from yarns and marine shop) they quarrelled about the respective merits of the Cocornut tree and the Plantain. Dampier, as a West Indian sailor, extolled the plantain, with (apparently) 'all the art of Rhetoricke and Logicke.' Knox, as an East Indian sailor, got extremely hot and prickly whenever a plantain tree was mentioned. 'It is,' he says, 'no more proper to call them trees than it is to Call a Cabbage a tree ... whare as the Cocornut tree Contineweth flourishing about 100 yeares.' Knox had neither Rhetoricke nor Logicke, only a passion 'to doe the Cocornut tree justice' and a kind of native wildness in his spelling.

They were remarkable-looking men, as remarkable men invariably are. Dampier, probably the taller of the two, was of a black, forbidding beauty, with a clear skin, showing scarlet under tan. Knox, a stumpier figure, had the battered, triumphant look of one who, after a long struggle for salvation, has found his calling and election sure. His weather-beaten, manful old face is happy with the power of being fervent in season and out of season. If we may hazard an opinion, Dampier, who was not reared in the school of piety nor much touched by religious feeling, may have found his companion's pious ejaculations trying.

Knox was a captive among the natives in Ceylon for the best twenty years of his life, and his book is an account of his captivity, with some description of Ceylon as it was. 'Whether hereafter they are ever or never read by anyone it is equially the same to me,' he says. With a gush of the improving talk which he lets fly on these occasions, he tells us why it is the same. The burden of his song is very much – 'Man is dust. Man, thou art a Worm. Man, a century hence you will be equially the same, whether in six feet or the moles of Adrianus.' Probably he was not a gloomy man when he first went to sea. But to be ruined and kept in exile among an inferior race throws a man in upon himself; and Knox for many years led the life of the religious contemplative without the contemplative's solaces and safeguards. It would not be fair to say that he came home mad; but it is plain that he came home with the crankiness of one who has lived an abnormal life during many years. His crankiness showed itself in well-marked monkish ways, in a hatred of women (which was, perhaps, partly fear), and in an inability to mix on equal terms with his fellow-men. It is said that men who have been in prison for a long term never really rejoin their fellows. The spiritual experience to which the outer world has no key, and that self-created world which has served the soul for world for so long a time, forbid a perfect reunion. Knox came home from Ceylon with a world in his head, built up out of constant Bible-reading. Whenever he found that the men of the real world failed to understand him (and his constant quarrels and wrangles show that they failed pretty often) he turned to this imaginary world for justification and for solace. He sometimes moralizes very prettily on death, the futility of life, the vanity of human ambition, and the queerness of Fate's dealings. Bishops South and Atterbury did the like by us at even greater length. On the whole, Knox is better reading than the bishops, for at root he is a simple, hardy being who had had to fight to live, and for a companion in this world we prefer one who has had to depend first and last on what is manly in himself. For this reason Knox's moralizings are never quite tedious. One feels the man behind the writing. There is someone robust and sturdy at the back of it all. Life proved Knox to the bone before he earned his leave to write. A man so proved is genuine whether he be enlightened or not.

Knox was not enlightened. Like other unenlightened men, he finds it difficult to express himself. His book gives a reader the impression of an entirely sincere man entirely confused. It is as though a jumble of piety, avarice, suspicion, delicate noble feeling, utter callousness, and rule of thumb were hung upon a character essentially upright and simple. Now and then he is even heroic. One of his simple acts of piety strikes us as indescribably heroic. His father and he, with other members of the crew, went ashore on Ceylon and were captured by the Sinhalese. He was allowed to go back to the ship with a message. Before he set out with this message he promised his father that he would return. He could have escaped in the ship quite easily. Those on board the ship begged him to escape while he had the chance. He was a young man, why should he go back to captivity; why not get away in the ship now Providence had helped him to her? Knox delivered his message and went back to his father, and was a captive for the next twenty years.

Many of the sea captains of that age were men of fine mental attainments and great political sagacity. Their books are wise with the rough and noble wisdom of men who have faced big issues of life and death for months together. Knox's mind was too confused for wisdom. His piety, though great, provided him with no way of life. Newton, Cowper's friend, was changed by sudden religious illumination from a slaver to a preacher. Knox, on the other hand, having been brought, as he would put it, out of the Land of Egypt, became not a preacher but a slaver. He got a little ship full of powder and trade guns, and went away to Madagascar to buy slaves. On this voyage the man's character seems to have gone to pieces. It often happens that when the devil gets well he forgets to pay his doctor's bill. Knox as a slaver is not a pretty figure.

His trade lay with a certain King Ribassa, who 'was one of the younger Sonns of the famous old King Lightfoot, who with his owne hand would shoot those of his wives that offended him, and after bid some cut open her body to take out the Bullett.' This man, as was to be expected from his breeding, 'soone dranke up the Bottle of Brandy I sent him, and dispatched away my Messenger to mee againe with 6 Slaves (3 men and 3 Women) for a present to me . . . which I looked one as a presage of a successfull trade like to insew.' Indeed, in a little while comes the entry: 'We shooke hands and rubbed noses . . . and began to drinke Brandy which was the King's Chiefe delight.' During the drinking the King much admired Knox's big dog, 'as the Dog did the King to see him so full of Colours as his beads made him – for the King arose to stroake the Dog, which put the Doge into a fome with rage that I was faint to catch him about the Necke else he would have tasted what the fine King was made one.'

It is said that Courts give a tone to society. The following entry shows the fine flavour of Court life under Ribassa and his brother. 'The King and I walked hand in hand . . . with one hand he led me and in the other hand he held a bottle of Brandy, saying unto me as we walked "See how all obey my word," and when the work was done Prince Chemaniena came and licked his father's knees in testimony of his obedience, and helped us to drinke our bottle of Brandy.' The brandy was shed unavailingly. Ribassa was a knave, and his brother's charity was interrupted by pirates (whether Mission's or Avery's men does not appear). Knox had done a little piracy in his time, as 'this in all appearance seemed a ready way to raise my decayed fortune'; but being a pirate and being robbed by one do not leave the same flavour on the palate. He wisely set sail for far away Bencoulen, where 'about 20 men all looking like Ghoasts' lived in Dampier's old fort on rotten rice and punch.

Knox lived to be about eighty years old. After twenty years' captivity, a long battering at sea, yellow fever, scurvy, malaria, Hurry Canes, and other tumults, such an age does him credit. There can be no doubt that Defoe (who knew him) got many hints for 'Robinson Crusoe' from him. It is sad that the comparatively colourless Selkirk should have robbed him of much credit properly his.

Some forty odd years ago Mr James Ryan edited and printed his collected writings, together with an Autobiography never before published, from which some of these facts are quoted.

CAPTAIN JOHN COXON

Nine generations ago, the island of Carmen, in the Lagoon of Tides, in the Bay of Campeachy, was one of the loneliest places in the world. It was a wilderness, half swamp half jungle, where the red mangrove trees, and the stunted whitethorn, shut away a few Indians from the roaring of the Lagoon tides at flood and ebb.

To the north of it there lay the Bay, to the south the Lagoon; to the west and east a number of sandy islands about which the tides raced. On some of the islands, and on all the marshy mainland, there grew the valuable logwood-trees, which made the neighbouring waters to smell sweetly when their profuse yellow blossoms were in season. To these islands, at certain times of the year, there came a Spaniard from Campeachy, with a gang of cow-boys, to hunt the wild cattle for their hides and tallow. This Spaniard, whose name was Juan de Acosta, was the only white man who ever came there. How the cattle got there will never be known; but it is to be supposed that they had strayed from the Spanish settlements, and multi-plied, and at last swum across to the islands at low water.

During the first ten years of the reign of Charles II a buccaneer ship, cruising far to 'leeward,' discovered the Lagoon, and explored its shores. Her seamen found sev-eral belts of logwood near the salt creeks, and took some stacks of the timber to Port Royal, where they sold it at a good price. After that, several ships (both merchant ships and buccaneer cruisers) went thither yearly to load log-wood for Jamaica. The wood, which was then much used for dyeing, sold for from £15 to £70 a ton in the English markets. It could be had for the cutting all about the Lagoon of Tides, while the great plenty of fruit and cattle thereabouts made the business inexpensive. Perhaps no people since the beginning of time have shown so evident a fondness for free quarters and large profits as the buccaneers displayed at this period of their history. The business of logwood cutting suited them very well, for it did not necessarily interfere with their rightful calling; while the title 'logwood cutter' looked rather better on a Charge Sheet. Very soon the creeks of the Lagoon were peopled by little settlements of buccaneers, who built themselves huts of palm leaves, and laboured very hard at their new craft. Many of them stayed there all the year round, cutting timber and stacking it, and selling it to the merchant ships which came thither from Port Royal. They lived together in little gangs, with their common casks of rum and sugar, and such wives as they could buy in Jamaica, or steal from the local Indians. They called the present Carmen Island Beef Island, and made some arrangement with Juan de Acosta for the slaughtering of the beeves for their food. Five days in each week they cut logwood. On the sixth they took their guns and went hunting. The seventh they observed as the Sabbath. When a ship came to the Lagoon all work was laid aside. The cutters went aboard her, and passed the rest of the day in drinking her commander's rum and firing off her guns. If the captain were sparing of his rum and powder, they gave him a cargo of bad wood. Thus did they encourage a generous spirit and a virtuous liberality among their patrons. All this is by way of prelude, or prologue, to the history we propose to present.

In the years 1669 and 1670 two Englishmen, brothers, named John and William Coxon, began business as logwood merchants, trading between Port Royal and the Lagoon of Tides. With William Coxon we have no concern; but we may take it for granted that at this time both he and his brother were fairly virtuous. Had they been otherwise, they would hardly have gone trading at a time when Henry Morgan was about to march on Panama. We surmise that John Coxon was then a young man, and (very possibly) new to the Indies. He was one of the first to enter into friendly relations with Juan de Acosta. We may be sure that he was very prodigal in rum and powder, and that the 'Old Standards,' the senior lumbermen, always laid by for him the choicest wood. He passed his days between the Lagoon and Port Royal, making perhaps two trips in each year. But in the summer of 1672 the Spaniards began to look with disfavour upon the growing trade in the Bay. Juan de Acosta was accused of encouraging the English, and cast into prison at Campeachy. One or two trading ketches, laden with supplies of logwood, were snapped up by Spanish 'Armadillies,' while the Spanish guarda-costas, from San Juan de Ulloa, received orders to destroy any logwood cutter's settlement which they could find. John Coxon was troubled by these gentry, and lost a part of his business. The Jamaican Government could not allow him to make reprisals; nor was it strong enough to protect a station so far away as the Lagoon. The Governor gave order that in future all logwood ships were to sail in fleets not less than four ships strong. This arrangement worked fairly well, until the final destruction of the logwood industry a few years later.

After 1672 the Bay of Campeachy attracted large numbers of buccaneers, who found the 'windward' seas too hot to hold them. The camps in the Lagoon of Tides became rather more riotous than they had been. The lumbermen began to make forays along the coasts, when business was slack, with the result that their virtuous members became 'debauched' into 'wickedness.' We fear that one of the first to be 'debauched' was John Coxon. By 1675 he had left the logwood business. He had gathered together a crew of 'Privateers,' and had sailed to the island of Tortuga, where, for a sum down, a compliant French Governor gave him a commission to make 'war' upon the Spaniards, with the 'right' of landing 'to hunt' on Spanish territory. With this precious 'protection' in his pocket, John Coxon cut himself temporarily adrift from virtuous living. He hoisted the red flag, and set sail.

We do not know how he began his privateering; but we are forced to conclude that he wasted little time. By August 1676, he had been declared a pirate; and the Jamaican Government had offered mercy to all his men if they would deliver up their captain. To their credit, they refused this offer; but Coxon seems to have taken it as a hint to keep clear of Port Royal, and of the windward waters generally, till some other pirate had put him out of mind for the time being. Probably he went to some quiet place like Boca del Toro, off Nicaragua, where he could live upon turtle and manatee, and dice with his officers for tots of rum. He lay low, in this way, for nearly nine months.

His next appearance was in June or July 1677. He was then in command of about 100 Englishmen, who had taken as their allies some three or four French captains, with commissions from Tortuga. He induced these Frenchmen to come with him to attack Santa Martha, a strong little city not far from Cartagena, which had proved too strong for the buccaneers, though it had surrendered, twenty years before, to an English squadron. Drake had been driven from Santa Martha, so that there was a certain amount of glory to be won there. It could not be approached easily from the landward, and the defences to the sea-approach were powerful. Coxon was not dismayed by the difficulties it presented. He rowed in boldly in the early morning, a little before the dawn, and carried the main fort with a rush, while the garrison were sleeping.

The town was taken after a little fighting in the streets. All the credit of the capture was due to Coxon, who 'did all,' with his Englishmen, before the Frenchmen ventured to come ashore. At least, this was what he told Sir Thomas Lynch on his return to Port Royal. The plunder of Santa Martha was 'nothing to babble about.' It came to £20 a man, in 'money and broken plate'; though Coxon's share came to rather more. He brought away with him the Governor and the Bishop of the city, both of whom he held to ransom. There must have been something charming in him, for when he came to Port Royal to surrender to the Government (and to pay his tenths and fifteenths), the 'good old man' (the Bishop) expressed himself 'exceedingly satisfied' with his treatment. He expressed himself thus to Sir Thomas Lynch, who had come aboard to inquire after him, and to make him more comfortable, and to treat for his release. When he spoke, the entire buccaneer crew was lying on the deck blind drunk, and perhaps few bishops would have shown such charitable broadmindedness in such a situation, and at such a time.

The ransoms of the Bishop and the Governor were duly paid, and Coxon found himself rich enough to take advantage of an Act of Oblivion. For nearly two years he lived honestly in Jamaica; but (as he confessed) he then 'grew weary' of being honest (probably he ran short of money), so that he put to sea again in command of a small cruiser. In the summer of 1679 he was on the coasts of Honduras, where he made a great haul of indigo, tortoiseshell, cacao and cochineal. He would have preferred pieces of eight, but the homely proverb, 'it is not always May,' was doubtless a consolation to him. He smuggled much of his booty into Jamaica, where he flooded all the markets, and ruined half the dry-goods merchants. Then he set sail again (December 1679) to Negril Bay, at the west end of Jamaica, to fill provisions for a raid along the Spanish coasts. With him were Captains Sawkins and Sharp, both of whom have their niches in the sinks and cellars of Fame's temple. While they lay at Negril, a small trading ketch put in and anchored by them. She was going to leeward, to trade among the Moskito Indians. Aboard her was William Dampier, a merchant and logwood cutter, who was trying to make a little money, before he returned to England. The crew of the ketch promptly volunteered to join the buccaneers; so that Dampier 'was, in a manner, forced' to join them also. About Christmas 1679, Coxon made sail, and steered away to the Main, with designs upon the town of Porto Bello, where Drake had died, some eighty-three years before. Coxon took 200 men ashore, and marched for three days through swamps and woods, till on the dawn of the fourth he came to the city, and rushed it, as he had rushed Santa Martha. Porto Bello had been squeezed by the velvet glove of Henry Morgan in 1668, but Coxon's men secured booty which 'wacked up' to £30 or £40 a man. This was 'good gains,' and with this they were content. They rejoined their ships and sailed to Golden Island, a noted haunt of the buccaneers, in the 'Samballoes,' or Mulatas Islands, where they planned to cross the Isthmus of Darien, to plunder Santa Maria, a gold-mine near the South Seas. When they mustered at Golden Island, Coxon was in a ship of 80 tons, manned by 97 men.

The story of that crossing of the Isthmus has been told by many writers, four of whom were in the ranks at the time. At the landing, Captain John Coxon commanded the fifth and sixth companies, both of which marched under red colours. The colours were probably petticoats, which could afterwards be traded to the natives. Coxon landed in a bad mood, because he was not the chief commander of the expedition; that post having fallen to Richard Sawkins, a valorous imp of fame who was more popular than he. Two days after landing he had 'some

Words' with another company commander, one Peter Harris, a Kentish gentleman. On this occasion he so far forgot himself as to say D—n, and to whip up a gun and to fire at Peter Harris, who was by no means backward in retaliating. However, another company captain 'brought him to be quiet,' and so the voyage continued. Santa Maria was duly captured, 'but when they got there, the cupboard was bare,' for the month's take of gold had just been sent to Panama. This disappointment caused the buccaneers much annoyance. Some were for returning to their ships at Golden Island. Others, more venturous, were for attacking Panama. Coxon, who had taken Santa Martha and Porto Bello, was for returning to the ships, because, he argued, the honour of any further exploit, in this galère, will fall, not to me, but to Richard Sawkins. However, Sawkins was not so covetous of honour as Coxon thought. He caused the buccaneers to make Coxon their Admiral in his stead; which was promptly done, 'Coxon seeming to be well satisfied.' Then they embarked in 'canoas and periagoes' and rowed away west for Panama. On St George's Day (1680) the canoas of Sawkins and Coxon fought and defeated a Spanish squadron near the island of Perico. The battle was well-contested and abominably bloody; and the laurels were won by Richard Sawkins, who captured the Spanish admiral. This was a sore blow to Coxon, who now determined to return to his ship. Some of Sawkins's men 'stickled not to defame or brand him with the note of cowardice,' crying out that he had been backward in the battle, and that he wasn't half the Admiral he gave out. At this, Coxon took leave of the fleet, with some seventy hands. He took with him a ship and a periagua, which, as Sharp, his shipmate says, 'will not much Redound to his Honour.' He recrossed the Isthmus without trouble; rejoined his ship at Golden Island; and again went cruising along the Main.

Shortly after his return to the North Sea, he decided to row far up the Gulf of Darien to get gold from the Indians of those parts. He caused his seamen to cut up a useful suit of sails and to make a number of strong canvas bags (a bag apiece) for the ready conveyance of the gold, when it had been 'purchased,' or 'conveyed.' But though he rowed with creditable perseverance, 'with an astonishing Degree of Enthusiasm,' under a sun that was hot and through an atmosphere that was nearly liquid, he got no gold whatsoever. He could not even get any Indians to sell in Port Royal; for the Indians were not only 'Shy,' but 'Treacherous'; and had a way of potting your pirate, through a blowpipe, from behind a tree. Plainly, such Indians were best left alone by a force which, however civilized, lacked machine-guns. They wished these Indians might some day come into the hands of the Spaniards. Then, they argued, they wouldn't be so perky with their blowpipes, nor yet so suspicious of those who were really their best friends. Thus growling, they rowed out of the Gulf, and set sail for Jamaica. On the way, an English frigate chased them for a day or more, to give them a relish of the sweets of liberty.

We do not know what John Coxon did for the next few months. He probably cruised along the Main, taking what he could, and lying up, among the Mulatas Islands, when weary of the sea. He was at anchor at one of the Mulatas Islands in May 1681, when Dampier arrived there, after his tramp across the Isthmus. He was then in very good fettle, and did not want hands. With him were several other buccaneers, French, Dutch, and English, who were planning a 'concerted piece,' or buccaneer orchestral effect, which should startle the Spaniards extremely. However, it came on to blow; the ships were separated; the great scheme came to nothing; and Coxon disappears again, under storm-staysails, for the best part of a year. In June or July 1682, he turned up at the Bahama Group, at the office of the Governor of New Providence. He explained that he wanted a commission to enable him 'to make war on the Spaniards of Cuba, St Augustine, and others'; which commission (to his great surprise) was promptly granted. He recruited at New Providence, by the simple method of inviting defaulting debtors to come aboard. Then he sailed to Jamaica, apparently to show Sir Thomas Lynch what a beautiful commission he had gotten from Bahama. Sir Thomas reproved the too trusting official, and diverted honest Coxon's fervour into another channel, by bidding him go to Honduras to escort home some logwood merchants. Coxon gave up his intention of making war on the Spaniard, and sailed to Honduras to do this, but, unfortunately, his men had little heart for convoy duty. Being Government men, at £1 a month and their victuals, was less pleasant, and infinitely less glorious, than being 'on the account' for 'whatever they could rob.' They plotted to heave John Coxon into the gulf, and to run away with the ship, 'and go privateering.' So they came aft in a body to put their bloody resolutions into effect. 'But he valiantly resisted, killed one or two with his own hand, forced eleven overboard, and brought three to Port Royal,' where they were condemned and hanged. This action so delighted Lynch that he made Coxon his trusted henchman. Early in 1683, Lynch sent him out again, this time to his old ally, Captain Yanky-Dutch, with an offer of '£200 in Gold, besides Victuals,' if, between them, they could capture the French privateer *La Trompeuse*, commanded by their whilom friend, Captain Peter Paine.

Virtue so fervent as that of John Coxon soon burns itself out. The pure flame which forced eleven mutineers into the sea in November 1682, was but a smoke and a memory a year later. In a letter dated November 1683, we find the curt entry, 'Coxon is again in rebellion'; while another, of March 1684, describes him as cruising off the Terra

Firme. Then a vagrant impulse to virtue drove him back to Jamaica, where he found a surety, and some honest employment, which kept him ashore, but only for a little while. In January 1686, he returned to Jamaica from another piratical raid, the details of which are missing. He claimed on this occasion to be weary of piracy; but the authorities were more weary than he, so he was laid by the heels, and sent for trial at St Jago del la Vega, 'where there will be few sympathizers among the jury.' Those who are to be tried in a place where there will be few sympathizers among the jury, have every incentive to find sympathizers in the gaol. Coxon discovered the practical virtues of this statement. He got away from the prison before the jury was called; and he was next heard of in Campeachy, cutting logwood, and raiding the coasts. A ship was sent after him; but this ship, though she captured some of his men, failed to take him. In 1687 he was still cruising, and making a good deal of money 'by snapping up Indians to sell.' In 1688, for some reason, he again surrendered at Jamaica to the Duke of Albemarle, who 'sent him to Lynch' in despair.

We do not know how he escaped hanging; but the stars in their courses fought for him, and he got off somehow. He had still ten years of life before him; and these he passed quietly, as a trader to the Moskito shore. At times the old Adam rose up strongly in him; and then he would gather the Indians together, and take them to the Spanish settlements, 'surprizing them in the night,' as he had once surprised Santa Martha. 'This Coxon encouraged the Indians to such practices.' He died among them, surrounded by 'wild Indian slaves and harlots,' in the year 1698. The Indians sorrowed for him 'after their manner'; and three old English pirates, who lived in that strange place, helped dig his grave; and then drank a cup of rum to his memory, and fired a French volley to his wandering shadow.

IN A CASTLE RUIN

'Very long ago,' said the old man, 'the castle was owned by a Scotchman named Carr, whose daughter was the most beautiful woman in the world. The name of this daughter was Clelia. She married Andy MacDonnell, who came over at the time of the Settlement; and after her marriage she lived on at the castle with her husband, helping Carr with the land. When Andy had been married about half a year, he was called away to Scotland on business; for he was a great man in Scotland, and at that time there was to be marrying between the royal families of Scotland and England, and he was wanted to carry a banner at the wedding. So he went to Scotland. And when they heard he was coming back they made all ready for a feast, and they had fires lighted, and all the fiddlers and the pipers came; and the poets came from the back hills making up new songs.

'Now at last, the ship which brought Andy MacDonnell came round the Point yonder, and Andy got ashore, and then the ship rowed away. Then Carr went up to him and asked why he was turning the ship away again. "Isn't that the ship you sailed in?" he said. "Isn't that your own ship?" "It is not," says Andy. "My own ship's in Scotland. The King took a fancy to her." So then Carr asked him what had become of all the men who had gone with him abroad. And he answered that the King had taken a fancy to them, and that they were all with the King in Scotland, every man jack of them down to Johnny O'Hara, the piper's boy. So Carr wondered a little at that,

97

but said nothing; and they all went up to the castle to the feast.

'But there was a queer thing that was noticed. There was a little lad of the MacLearnon's running about bare foot among the horses. He was a little wee lad, the nicest little lad you would be seeing. So when Andy MacDonnell was coming to the castle from the shore, this little Mac-Learnon looks at him; and he was near him; and he said to his mother, "His Honour's ears is pointed." They were pointed just the same as the ears on a terrier. Wasn't it wonderful that no one had ever noticed that before; that he should have pointed ears, and no one see it? I'm thinking that was a great wonder.

'Now after that, things settled down as before. Andy MacDonnell lived on with Carr at the Castle, and there was nothing much happened, except a little child was born to Clelia; and that was a queer thing, the child was. It was a little wee man of a child, and he was born with teeth in him, and the first thing his mother saw of him was that his ears were pointed; and the nurses said that that was a great shame, and she so beautiful a mother. There were other things, besides that, which seemed queer. Andy MacDonnell was another sort of a man than he had been. He used to go up beyond, in the back hills, at the time of a new moon. He got a bad name on to him for doing that; but that was nothing to what they caught him doing another time on the back hills, beyond the wood there. There's a flat place there, where they used to hold cock fights in the old times. It was a religious place before that, where they did the old religion, and there's wraiths in it, besides Themselves; and it was there they caught Andy. It was one twilight they caught him. He was standing on the grass, bowing to a great black goat; and every time he bowed the goat spoke to him in ancient Irish. Wasn't that a wonderful thing now? There was a strong magic in that;

indeed there was. The shepherds didn't say anything, for Andy was a great gentleman, but they thought it a queer thing, for all that. And Carr kept wondering all the time what had become of the ship, and all the men left behind in Scotland.

'Now just about a year after Andy MacDonnell had come home, he and Carr, and Clelia and the child were sitting on the grass (on a carpet) looking out over the bay, and it was one evening, getting towards sunset; and as they were sitting talking, they saw a small boat pulling in to the bay, and Carr said, "It's a tired man in that boat," for he was pulling like a crazy man. And Clelia said, "It'll be some poor man who has maybe lost his ship." And Andy MacDonnell looked hard at the boat, and says he, "I'll be going in," he said, "the evening strikes cold," he says. So he turned, and went into the house. There was no one ever saw him again.

'Now the boat ran ashore on the beach, and the tired man got out of her, just by those rocks; and he was tired indeed. He could scarce climb up that bank of shingle. So Carr looks hard at him. "Why," he says, "it's Johnny O'Hara, the piper's boy, that was left behind in Scotland. What news, Johnny!" he says. So Johnny comes near up to him, and, "Bad news," he says. "It's bad news I'm bringing you this day. Your man is killed," he says. "Andy MacDonnell is killed," he says. "He was killed by the Scotch the day he was to have come home. And I've been a prisoner ever since." So Carr got up on his feet, and he calls out "Andy"; but no one ever came. And Clelia called out "Andy"; but no one ever answered. And they went into the castle, but no Andy was there, and then they knew that they'd been living with a dragon-man, and that the real Andy had been dead a year. When Clelia knew that she'd been living with a dragon-man, she went upstairs to her room, and took out a kind of dirk she had, with a sharp point on it, and she said a prayer first, and then stuck herself, so that she fell dead. That was in one of the top chambers. It's all fallen in now, this long time; but that was where she killed herself. And when Carr knew that there had been a dragon-man, he looked at the child, and he knew it for a dragon-child, because its ears was pointed, so he took it up and swung it against the tower wall, against these corner stones, until he had it killed. Then he went down the strand yonder, to that point of rocks below my cabin, and there he drowned himself. That's why the point is called Carr's Point, to this day. He was the last man to live in the castle here. No one would ever live in it after that, and the floors fell in, and the woodwork was taken; and now there's the ivy on it.'

A DEAL OF CARDS

A company of seamen sat round a cabin table, and pledged each other in a brew of punch. They sat upon locker tops, on cushions of green velvet gone rusty at the seams. The stern-ports were open at their backs, for it was hot, and the room between decks was foul with the reek of their tobacco. You could tell that the ship was under way by glancing astern at the dull track, like a great snail's track, which she had drawn upon the blue water as she dragged in the light wind. She rolled slightly now and again, making a creaking in her gear, and trembling the silver lamp upon the cabin bulkhead. She was an old ship, you could see by the rot upon the beams. She was foul with a long passage, and the cabin reeked of bilge. The blue arras on the cabin door was wormy with age. The parquetting in her deck was dirty with the marks of sea-boots. It was heaped here and there with a sort of loot, such as clothes with lace upon them, and small arms, cheap jewellery, buckles, and the like, for the cruise had been lucky in a way. Two of the seamen at the rum were dicing each other, for some uncut stones in a packet from the mines of Esmeralda.

The drinkers were silent for the most part, puffing out their tobacco like a gang of Spaniards, only speaking to call a health, such as, 'A fair slant,' or 'Dollars,' or to mark the throw of the dice. They were a rough lot of fellows, some of them branded in the cheeks. Most of them had scars about their faces, and not one of them but carried arms – pistols, or a dirk, or a seaman's hanger – in a belt of

coloured leather, plaited by the wearer. One of the number had his head in a rag, and swore thickly from time to
time, as though his wound were painful. He had been hurt
with a knife by a mate that morning, since when he had
been at the rum. His head was singing like a kettle, what
with the cut, the drink, and the heat of the between decks.
His name was Joe; he was a runaway from a king's ship,
once a sailor trading out of Bristol.

Perhaps he was a little touched with fever, for of a
sudden he refilled his pannikin and drank it dry. He rose
unsteadily, clutching at the table, and at the shirts of his
companions. He leaned his head through the window,
flinging his empty can far astern into the still, blue sea.

'A rot on all salt water,' he shouted. Then he collapsed
over a Newgate man, who had long hoed tobacco in the
Indies. Blood was trickling from under his rag, for the
wound was broken out again. A little blood came from
between his lips: he seemed in a bad way. He had had
some sort of a stroke.

'Joe's got the shakes,' said the Newgate man. 'Help us
hold of him, Bill; lay him among them prettiments.'

He pointed to the loot on the deck. One of the dicers
took hold of Joe's boots, and dragged him clear of the
table. They dropped him roughly among the clutter, with
his head on some lace. The Newgate man went through
his pockets. There were only two copper charms, some
tobacco plug, a steel for striking a light, and a ball of twine.

'He diced it all,' said Bill, 'that time we stuck him with
the Greeks.'

'I'll throw you for the plug,' replied the Newgate man.
'He'll do now. He's only in some sort of a fit.'

They then returned to the rum.

When Joe fell across the convict his eyes were burning
in a mist of blood, which seemed to shoot and shake in
front of him. His ears were drumming, as though a bird

were beating his head with wings, and he felt that he was dropping from a height into some deep, empty well. In a little time the red mist cleared away; the drumming hushed; the feeling of dropping changed. He was in a little dark room, before a fire of embers, which made a red glow upon the chimney bricks. It was a lonely little room, darker than the night, but for the coals, and so still it might have been below the ground, below the graves even, beneath the dead with their glazed eyes. So utterly silent it was, he was glad to hear his heart beat. It beat steadily, like a menace, like the continual tapping of a drum. It was beating, not like a heart, but like a clock. Like some clock in hell ticking to the souls among the fire. It was ticking like the march of time through the dim roads of eternity. It was a thing horrible, inexorable, that continual ticking. In the blackness, the utter silence, that beating music became terrible. It seemed to fill the room. It seemed to roar about his body like a crowd of spirits about a corpse. He tried to shake himself, but could not stir. He tried to cry aloud, but could not speak. He tried to arrest his heart, to stop that ticking. But it beat on, rhythmical, steady, terrible. It seemed that the darkness, the noise, the glowing coals, were laughing at him.

And then, with a great burst, the ticking ceased and the room became quite light – as light, he thought, as a summer day at noon. Where the fire had burned a woman squatted, a black woman, black as coal, in a plain gown of scarlet. Her eyes burned in an intense and baleful brightness. Her lips were apart, showing white teeth in a grin. In her hand she held cards.

He looked at these cards. Indeed, she held them towards him for him to see, turning them over that he might see both sides of them. They were three in number, and each of them had a black back, as black as a piece of ebony. The faces were coloured in intense colours, one of gold, which seemed to burn, one of crimson, which glowed, one of black, which seemed angry like the smoke of hell. The colours of them seemed to be the tokens of a beauty, a fierceness and a horror, beyond any words that he could fashion.

The black woman grinned at him as she thrust the cards together. She crouched down upon the hearth, purring like a cat, cackling, whining. Her eyes gleamed as she began to shuffle the cards, tossing them in the air, passing, re-passing, whirling them about, till they seemed like three arrows of red and gold and black fire. At last she flung them all into the air, caught them in one hand as they fell, bowed very low, her lips grinning, her eyes intensely bright, and held them out, face downwards, for him to make his choice. All that he could see were three black cards, spread out before him like the sticks of a fan. Yet he knew that upon his choice of a card depended his life, his life hereafter, the life of his soul between the lives.

'No,' he tried to gasp. 'No, I will not choose.'

The little black hag laughed. She whirled the cards into the air, and watched them fly away, like birds, crying strange words as they flew. The room burst into a million fragments, flinging Joe into the night. The light grew very violent of a sudden, and there he was, feeling mortal sick, lying in the sunlight, in the cabin, with an Indian splashing water on him.

They made the three Points the next morning, and were at anchor in the bay beyond them before noon. It was broiling hot. The sea lay like a mass of hot grease. The dark green feathers on the palms seemed drooped for the lack of freshness. One heard nothing save the roaring of the surf, the birds screaming in the wood, and the perpetual groaning of the ship. She rolled heavily, banging her gear in a continual clatter. Her blocks were whining like dogs. The noise of her was like a hammer on the brain.

Joe volunteered for the boat, and went ashore with the water-casks the moment the anchor held. He had been fuddled ever since the day before, and the ship had such terrors for him, drunk as he was, there was no staying aboard her. On the beach he met Willy Crackers, an old English sailor, who lived in the huts above the surf line. He was a bronzed, ear-ringed man, was Willy, with a bright eye to him and a tongue of silver. He had been in that land many years now, and owned several slaves. He used to get gold dust and ivory from the inland, to trade with the ships which touched the coast. He was a friend to the pirates, and they used to water there before dropping down to leeward. He returned to England in time a rich man, and died in Salcombe the keeper of a sailor's tavern. He greeted Joe kindly, and the two stayed together all day, in the blazing heat, watching the natives fill the water-casks and stow them in the jolly boat. But at sunset, when the jolly boat went off, when the beach struck cold, and the mists rose whitely, Willy bade Joe come up to the hut for a bite of supper and a smoke.

The house was a ramshackle affair, built in one storey alongside the huts. It swung some three hammocks, all draped with netting. It had a table much eaten by the ants, a bench or two, some casks of ship's provisions (which might have sailed with Hawkins), a pipe of rum, a few teeth, most of them a little yellow, and some weapons, beautifully bright, in a trophy rack upon the wall. Towards midnight, Willy got up to fetch his mate a curio.

'Some heathen idol,' he said, 'them blacks give it to me for a whittle.'

It had been placed behind some barrels, and what with the rum, what with a long spell of laziness, Willy was unable to shift them. Joe came to his assistance, canted the casks, and rolled them away upon their chines.

'Thankee, mate,' said Willy, 'I'm not so limber as I was.

I been ashore too long. Me joints is gone in the slings.' He paused awhile. Then he piped out, 'Mate, matey, supposin' you was to stop ashore with me. There ain't no call for you to go a-cruising. I'd be proud to have you. Hell,' he continued, 'I can't rastle them blacks. I want some one spryer'n myself. Some one as'll fly their hides, by Davy.'

There was a pause for a moment, while Joe's heart leaped with pleasure. He had been taken with so great a horror of the ship, since the vision of the hag, that his muddled brain had planned suicide, or a life in the scrub among the blacks, rather than another day between decks. The words of Willy Crackers lit up his brain. They showed him the ease, the grandeur of the life of nigger driver. The joyful nights over the jorum; the English ship; the thronged quays of Bristol. He took the offer with a curse.

'Billy,' he said, 'it'll be meat and drink to me. I ain't been feeling good these last days. Going to sea ain't right for me. It's the air or something. A spell ashore is what I want: just what I want – that, and sleep. I'll get my chest ashore when the cutter comes in for the casks tomorrow.'

'Why, right then,' said his friend, 'you look pretty green in the gills with it. And now let's liquor on it.'

He poured out two more noggins from the pan, and the two drank to each other.

'There's a song I mind me,' said Joe, 'I'll sing it to ye.'

He began to sing in a voice a little muffled with the rum. He dwelt upon each word, singing it with gusto.

O, the bold Lollonais, so gall-ant and free,
He sailed from Saint James in the Jane chasse-marree,
   Oh, there's rum and there's wine
   And tobacco so fine
For all the bold sailors what sails on the sea.

He sang the refrain twice over, hammering on the table with his can. He was reaching out for another tot of rum when he fell forward gasping. His pannikin fell from the table and rolled away among the gear. Willy blinked at him for a moment, beating out the chorus with his pipe. He thought his mate was merely overcome with the spirit. He made a childish attempt to reach the jorum for another taste, and fell asleep in his chair, his pipe's ash spilling sparks upon the table. The lamp flared up a moment to show the couple to the night, and then guttered out, leaving them to their quiet.

It seemed to Joe that he was bound upon the rim of a whirlpool of flame. He was being spun about a vortex, helpless as a straw; gradually the spinning became swifter, as though he had been whirled nearer to the centre. Then tiny hands seemed to pluck him down into a pit of utter silence, a light broke upon him, and there, in front of him, was the malevolent woman of the cards. She grinned at him with her brilliant teeth, and held out two cards – one black, the other crimson. Soon she began to shuffle with them, tossing them from one hand to the other, throwing them at her victim, then snatching them away. At last she caught them, whirled them round her, bowed very low, and held them forward, face downwards, watching him intently with a malignant smile.

'No,' he gasped: 'No, I will not choose.'

Instantly she screamed in her high, mocking laugh. She tossed the cards from her, and they whirled away, crying like gulls. The whirlpool spun him upward, flinging him upon a sea alive with sharks. He leaped from them, screaming, running violently upon the air; but they rose after him, flapping their fins, gnashing their teeth. They were barking at him like dogs, snapping at his very feet. Then he fell, fell, fell, till he was as a drop of water gaped at by all the damned among the fire.

He awoke upon the hut floor, in plain day, the blood beating on his brain, the surf roaring. A boat was pulling in from the ship, the oars keeping time to an old hauling tune. Willy Crackers was snoring in his chair, and after trying to rouse him, Joe helped himself to about a pint of rum and staggered out upon the beach. The terror of his sleep was strong upon him. The palm leaves, dangling green and heavy, were a horror to him. The surf terrified him. In every creeper of the jungle he saw the eyes of the devil with the cards. Not for a sack of minted gold would he have stayed in that place. So when the boat made the landing he tumbled into her, and fell asleep, in a drunkard's doze, among the breakers in the stern sheets. He did not rouse from where he lay until rough hands beat him with stretchers, and fierce voices bade him out of that. For the boat was alongside the ship, dragging to a tackle, and the ship was under a jib and topsail, forging slowly forward, while the hands were singing at the bows, heaving in the cable. They were under way.

He scrambled aboard, and went below to his hammock. He swung there all that day, hot with a violent fever, and now and again an Indian brought him drink. Just forward of where he lay, two fiddlers made music between the guns, and men sang and danced there till they were too drunk to stir. The ship picked up her consort that afternoon. They cruised together till the sunset, when they made the Gabone River. They anchored at about ten that night in the anchorage by Parrot Island.

In the morning of the second day, Joe sat between two cannon on a lashed sea chest, which had his initials, J.P., burnt deeply upon the lid. He had a canvas sack in front of him, for he was busy packing, and he had been dicing for the loot due to him ever since his morning draught. He had made up his mind to quit that way of life and get ashore to the island. There were folk living on the island – a sort of traders. He could stay with them, he thought, till a home-bound ship happened into the river. He had money enough. And, once in England, there was always work for a live one. Ever since he had had these visions, a terror of the sea and the ships had made his life a burden. Drink, even, had no comforts for him; for, from the hatchways, from the dark places behind the guns, from the hold where the casks lay, he would see peering that black hag of the tarot. So he had gathered his gear together, and was going ashore in ten minutes' time, to live among the traders till a ship came. He would live cleanly, too, without rum, except in the way of friendship. His head wasn't what it was. It was no use going on drinking when one saw things.

'You give me that knife, Jake Dawes,' he said, 'and I'll throw you in a quart of hard.'

Jake tossed the knife to him, a long Spanish dirk, with a handle of twisted silver, like those you buy in Panama. There was a noise on deck, a confused babble of cries and clanking.

'What in hell are they at, Jake?' he asked.

A man in a red shirt, a leather apron and sea boots made of cow-hide, came past them with a bucketful of wads.

'There's a fat merchant on the coast,' he said, 'we're going out for her. They're getting under way. The *Fortune*'s men are giving us a tow.'

'I'm off ashore,' said Joe. 'To blazes with this dicing. Give us a lift there, Billy, with these duds.'

'Oh, that be twisted, Joe,' said Jake, as he knocked off the neck of a bottle. 'Stop and drink fair.'

The mulatto grinned at him and handed him the spirits; Joe took a large swig.

'That's better, Jake,' he said; 'have you got a quid upon you?'

They spent the next twenty minutes drinking in turn, and chewing meditatively upon the quid. The ship was under way, with her topsails set, dropping slowly down the stream. The *Fortune*'s men, very drunk, had cast the ropes off and gone splashing back to moorings. Through an open gun-port Joe caught a glimpse of moving palms.

'Hell!' he cried, 'I'm off ashore. We're moving, Jakey.'

'The boats are gone by this,' said the mulatto, 'it's unchancy swimming. You'd better stay for the play.'

But Joe sprang to his feet, 'I'll swim it,' he cried, as he made a rush for the hatchway. As he passed the midship cannon, his foot caught in a ring bolt. He stumbled on a pace, flung up his hands and crashed heavily over the ranged port cable. He had been 'overtaken,' as the saying is. A man in a fine red coat, with laced cuffs, and buttons of gold pieces, came along the gun deck swearing. He was followed by another man brandishing a pistol.

'Get to your guns there, you swine!' the two were shouting. 'Cast loose them lower deck cannon! What corpse is this? What in hell corpse is this? Hey there, you, get the guns run out. We're going out for some yellow boys!'

They kicked at Joe's body in turn and passed over him to the groups of drunkards further forward. Away aft a gang of wits had cast loose a gun and were busy firing at the sky. On deck a seaman, bawling an obscene song, was running up the banner of the trade – a black banner, stolen from an undertaker, with two rude crimson figures roughly sewn upon its face. The chase was under all plain sail, some two miles distant, her decks full of men busy trimming her yards. The sailing master, watching her through a telescope from the fo'c's'le, declared her to be a French Guineaman, swimming deep. Another swore that she was out of Lisbon, a sugar ship bound home. The men hauled the spritsail yard alongships, crying out that they would have sweet punch for supper. The wind freshened. The men aloft loosed the top-gallant sails. The helmsman stood smoking at the tiller. On deck was nothing but a babble of cries, drowned every two or three minutes by the cannon.

But Joe lay where he had fallen, heedless of everything. When some men came to man the cannon at his side, they picked him up by the heels and lifted him below to the sail-locker. They flung him down upon a mainsail, and went back to their firing. They were all drunk and careless. And though, when the chase ran her guns out and hung out the King's colours, they made some sort of a battle of it, they were too drunk to do much. In a very few minutes their decks were being swept, their guns knocked over, their ports beaten from the side, and their men driven from their posts. The powder barrels exploded almost at each discharge, for the powder was in tubs about the deck, littered anyhow, and she was on fire in twenty places long before the crew surrendered.

It seemed to Joe that he was adrift in a torrent, flying down stream. It was all black about him, a blackness full of roaring; and water whirled in his mouth and nostrils till he choked. The roaring grew louder. He felt himself pitched downwards. A vast weight of water beat upon him, and then he was suddenly flung ashore in a cave, with pebbles at his feet and a great dread shaking him. It was dark enough, but not positively black, in the cave, for the low roof glittered with a metal, and the water was bright, in spangles, as it hurried past into the darkness. As he arose to his feet it grew lighter, and there was the little black hag again, in her red dress, with the bitter smile upon her lips. She burst into a harsh chattering laugh, like the rapid whirring of a cog-wheel. She spun round him once or twice gibbering with her lips. Then she stooped before him, plucked out a card, and thrust it into his hand with a mocking bow. He stared at it stupidly for a moment before he turned it over. It was a black card, black on both sides, of a black like the black of swirling smoke, and its blackness made him shudder. The hag watched his face a moment, and broke into a violent and mirthless merriment. Her face wrinkled in her laugh, and sharpened till she looked like a vulture rocking with some uncanny joy. Then she screamed in a long, shrill, wailing scream like the scream of night birds flying in a company. She tossed her hands upward, and it seemed to her victim that the wicked figure vanished through his eyes, and as though the skinny fingers clutched at his heart from inside him. In another second the cave had torn apart and flung him upward. He gave a gasp and a cry and awoke in the darkness of the sail-locker, in a silence only broken by scurrying rats and the dull gurgling of the bilge.

He picked himself up and went on deck, his head throbbing like a drum. He saw that the deck had been ripped with shot. Many bodies were lying on the planks. There was a smell of blood, of burning, of burnt linen, and powder smoke. The ship was unusually still, for the lower deck was empty save for the killed. He pushed up the hatchway in terror.

As he gained the upper deck he saw at once what had happened, for a big blue banner was flapping at the peak, and a few marines in red coats were watching the last gang of his comrades into a jolly boat alongside. They had been stripped already. Their silks and laces were dangling from their captors' pockets. A little lieutenant in a long red coat was superintending the embarkation, tapping his breeches with a cane to mark the number of them. Joe drew his hanger from its sheath.

'Taken!' he screamed, 'taken!' and he rushed at the lieutenant to cut him down.

A burly mariner in an apron bounded upon him from behind. Joe felt a blow upon the sconce, and collapsed upon the deck like a sack of flour.

'One hundred and three,' counted the lieutenant; 'that

was a good crack you gave him. Shove him down among the others.'

Late in the afternoon Joe woke from his fever. He was lying chained hand and foot in a dark prison lit only by a battle lamp. One side of him was pressed against the bulkhead of the prison; the other was riveted to a wounded man, a man in high fever, who babbled in his pain. He could distinguish other bodies lying near him.

'Where am I?' he cried.

'Hold your jaw!' said a hoarse voice, through the grating. 'Hold your jaw. You're aboard the frigate *Swallow*, if you want to know. And you'll be hanged for a damned rogue to-morrow dawn.'

THE DEVIL AND THE OLD MAN

Up away north, in the old days, in Chester, there was a man who never throve. Nothing he put his hand to ever prospered, and as his state worsened, his friends fell away, and he grew desperate. So one night when he was alone in his room, thinking of the rent due in two or three days and the money he couldn't scrape together, he cried out, 'I wish I could sell my soul to the devil like that man the old books tell about.'

Now just as he spoke the clock struck twelve, and, while it chimed, a sparkle began to burn about the room, and the air, all at once, began to smell of brimstone, and a voice said:

'Will these terms suit you?'

He then saw that some one had just placed a parchment there. He picked it up and read it through; and being in despair, and not knowing what he was doing, he answered, 'Yes,' and looked round for a pen.

'Take and sign,' said the voice again, 'but first consider what it is you do; do nothing rashly. Consider.'

So he thought awhile; then 'Yes,' he said, 'I'll sign,' and with that he groped for the pen.

'Blood from your left thumb and sign,' said the voice.

So he pricked his left thumb and signed.

'Here is your earnest money,' said the voice, 'nine and twenty silver pennies. This day twenty years hence I shall see you again.'

Now early next morning our friend came to himself and felt like one of the drowned. 'What a dream I've had,' he said. Then he woke up and saw the nine and twenty silver pennies and smelt a faint smell of brimstone.

So he sat in his chair there, and remembered that he had sold his soul to the devil for twenty years of heart's-desire; and whatever fears he may have had as to what might come at the end of those twenty years, he found comfort in the thought that, after all, twenty years is a good stretch of time, and that throughout them he could eat, drink, merrymake, roll in gold, dress in silk, and be care-free, heart at ease and jib-sheet to windward.

So for nineteen years and nine months he lived in great state, having his heart's desire in all things; but, when his twenty years were nearly run through, there was no wretcheder man in all the world than that poor fellow. So he threw up his house, his position, riches, everything, and away he went to the port of Liverpool, where he signed on as AB, aboard a Black Ball packet, a tea clipper, bound to the China seas.

They made a fine passage out, and when our friend had only three days more, they were in the Indian Ocean lying lazy, becalmed.

Now it was his wheel that forenoon, and it being dead calm, all he had to do was just to think of things; the ship of course having no way on her.

So he stood there, hanging on to the spokes, groaning and weeping till, just twenty minutes or so before eight bells were made, up came the Captain for a turn on deck.

He went aft, of course, took a squint aloft, and saw our friend crying at the wheel. 'Hello, my man,' he says, 'why, what's all this? Ain't you well? You'd best lay aft for a dose o' salts at four bells to-night.'

'No, cap'n,' said the man, 'there's no salts'll ever cure my sickness.'

'Why, what's all this?' says the old man. 'You must be sick if it's as bad as all that. But come now; your cheek is all sunk, and you look as if you ain't slept well. What is it ails you, anyway? Have you anything on your mind?

'Captain,' he answers very solemn, 'I have sold my soul to the devil.'

'Oh,' said the old man, 'why that's bad. That's powerful bad. I never thought them sort of things ever happened outside a book.'

'But,' said our friend, 'that's not the worst of it, Captain. At this time three days hence the devil will fetch me home.'

'Good Lord!' groaned the old man; 'Here's a nice hurrah's nest to happen aboard my ship. But come now,' he went on, 'did the devil give you no chance – no saving-clause like? Just think quietly for a moment.'

'Yes, Captain,' said our friend, 'just when I made the deal, there came a whisper in my ear. And,' he said, speaking very quietly, so as not to let the mate hear, 'If I can give the devil three jobs to do which he cannot do, why then, Captain,' he says, 'I'm saved, and that deed of mine is cancelled.'

Well, at this the old man grinned and said, 'You just leave things to me, my son. *I'll* fix the devil for you. Aft there, one o' you, and relieve the wheel. Now you run forrard, and have a good watch below, and be quite easy in your mind, for I'll deal with the devil for you. You rest and be easy.'

And so that day goes by, and the next, and the one after that, and the one after that was the day the devil was due.

Soon as eight bells was made in the morning watch, the old man called all hands aft.

'Men,' he said, 'I've got an all-hands job for you this forenoon.'

'Mr Mate,' he cried, 'get all hands on to the main-tops'l halliards and bowse the sail stiff up and down.'

So they passed along the halliards, and took the turns off, and old John Chantyman piped up –

> There's a Black Ball clipper
> Comin' down the river.

And away the yard went to the mast-head till the bunt-robands jammed in the sheave.

'Very well that,' said the old man. 'Now get my dinghy off o' the half-deck and let her drag alongside.'

So they did that, too.

'Very well that,' said the old man. 'Now forrard with you, to the chain-locker, and rouse out every inch of chain you find there.'

So forrard they went, and the chain was lighted up and flaked along the deck all clear for running.

'Now, Chips,' says the old man to the carpenter, 'just bend the spare anchor to the end of that chain, and clear away the fo'c's'le rails ready for when we let go.'

So they did this, too.

'Now,' said the old man, 'get them tubs of slush from the galley. Pass that slush along there, doctor. Very well that. Now turn to, all hands, and slush away every link in that chain a good inch thick in grease.'

So they did that, too, and wondered what the old man meant.

'Very well that,' cried the old man. 'Now get below all hands! Chips, on to the fo'c's'le head with you and stand by! I'll keep the deck, Mr Mate! Very well that.'

So all hands tumbled down below; Chips took a fill o' baccy to leeward of the capstan, and the old man walked the weather-poop looking for a sign of hell-fire.

It was still dead calm – but presently, towards six bells, he raised a black cloud away to leeward, and saw the

117

glimmer of the lightning in it; only the flashes were too red, and came too quick.

'Now,' says he to himself, 'stand by.'

Very soon that black cloud worked up to windward, right alongside, and there came a red flash, and a strong sulphurous smell, and then a loud peal of thunder as the devil steps aboard.

'Mornin', cap'n,' says he.

'Mornin', Mr Devil,' says the old man, 'and what in blazes do you want aboard *my* ship?'

'Why, Captain,' said the devil, 'I've come for the soul of one of your hands as per signed agreement: and, as my time's pretty full up in these wicked days, I hope you won't keep me waiting for him longer than need be.'

'Well, Mr Devil,' says the old man, 'the man you come for is down below, sleeping, just at this moment. It's a fair pity to call him up till it's right time. So supposin' I set you them three tasks. How would that be? Have you any objections?'

'Why no,' said the devil, 'fire away as soon as you like.'

'Mr Devil,' said the old man, 'you see that main-tops'l yard? Suppose you lay out on that main-tops'l yard and take in three reefs single-handed.'

'Ay, ay, sir,' the devil said, and he ran up the ratlines, into the top, up the topmast rigging and along the yard.

Well, when he found the sail stiff up and down, he hailed the deck:

'Below there! On deck there! Lower away ya halliards!'

'I will not,' said the old man, 'Nary a lower.'

'Come up your sheets, then,' cries the devil. 'This main-topsail's stiff up-and-down. How'm I to take in three reefs when the sail's stiff up-and-down?'

'Why,' said the old man, '*you can't do it*. Come out o' that! Down from aloft, you hoof-footed son. That's one to me.'

'Yes,' says the devil, when he got on deck again, 'I don't deny it, cap'n. That's one to you.'

'Now, Mr Devil,' said the old man, going towards the rail, 'suppose you was to step into that little boat alongside there. Will you please?'

'Ay, ay, sir,' he said, and he slid down the forrard fall, got into the stern sheets, and sat down.

'Now, Mr Devil,' said the skipper, taking a little salt spoon from his vest pocket, 'supposin' you bail all the water on that side the boat on to this side the boat, using this spoon as your dipper.'

Well! – the devil just looked at him.

'Say!' he said at length, 'which of the New England States d'ye hail from anyway?'

'Not Jersey, anyway,' said the old man, 'That's two up, all right; ain't it, sonny?'

'Yes,' growls the devil, as he climbs aboard. 'That's two up. Two to you and one to play. Now, what's your next contraption?'

'Mr Devil,' said the old man, looking very innocent, 'you see, I've ranged my chain ready for letting go anchor. Now Chips is forrard there, and when I sing out, he'll let the anchor go. Supposin' you stopper the chain with them big hands o' yourn and keep it from running out clear. Will you, please?'

So the devil takes off his coat and rubs his hands together, and gets away forrard by the bitts, and stands by.

'All ready, cap'n,' he says.

'All ready, Chips?' asks the old man.

'All ready, sir,' replies Chips.

'Then, stand by – Let *go* the anchor,' and clink, clink, old Chips knocks out the pin, and away goes the spare anchor and greased chain into a five mile deep of God's sea. As I said, they were in the Indian Ocean.

Well – there was the devil, making a grab here and a grab there, and the slushy chain just slipping through his claws, and at whiles a bight of chain would spring clear and rap him in the eye.

So at last the cable was nearly clean gone, and the devil ran to the last big link (which was seized to the heel of the foremast), and he put both his arms through it, and hung on to it like grim death.

But the chain gave such a *Yank* when it came-to, that the big link carried away, and oh, roll and go, out it went through the hawsehole, in a shower of bright sparks, carrying the devil with it. There is no devil now. The devil's dead.

As for the old man, he looked over the bows watching the bubbles burst, but the devil never rose. Then he went to the fo'c's'le scuttle and banged thereon with a hand-spike.

'Rouse out, there, the Port Watch!' he called, 'an' get my dinghy inboard.'

SOME FAMOUS WRECKS

Shipwrecks soon pass from human memory. Each decade knows a sad one, each generation a very fatal one. They are too frequently in the news to come much into history, unless they carry a prince like the White Ship or an Admiral with a name like Sir Cloudesley Shovell.

When I was young, sailors talked a good deal of only three wrecks, of the *Royal George*, the *Captain* and the *Eurydice*. Cowper's poem keeps the *Royal George* still in mind, but probably sailors now talk of much more recent losses, caused not by mishap and the fortune of the sea but enemy action.

Of the *Royal George*, the facts are partly known. One who went down with her and came up alive, a seaman named David Ingram, wrote a vivid and interesting pamphlet of his experience; and from his account the popular version of the loss is made.

The intake of the ship's sea-cock in one of the strakes below the water-line needed some repair. The ship, then lying at anchor at Spithead, had to be heeled, so that the carpenters might get at the fault. To heel the ship sufficiently, the starboard guns were run well inboard, and the work began. The ship had recently come in from a summer cruise; she was due for docking, and had been paid-off. She is supposed to have had about twelve hundred people on board her at the time, about a quarter of them women. As most of these tended to gather on the already listed port side they increased the list. The *Lark*, victualling sloop, was also on the port side, delivering stores to her. These weights as they swung on board also increased the list.

Presently the wind freshened slightly so that water began to fill the lower deck scuppers, splashing in from the scupper holes and over the port-sills. Ingram says that many mice were driven from their nests by this water, and that the seamen (amid the general disorder of paying-off) had much sport in striking at them, and perhaps drawing an even greater weight of persons to the listed side.

Ingram says that the officer of the watch delayed giving the order to correct the list by running back the starboard guns, and that some of the men, now scared by her heel, tried to run back the guns without waiting for the order.

Possibly a sudden gust of wind ended the matter, for she went over on her port side, filled, righted, and went down. There can be no doubt that she was exceedingly rotten, and that the final collapse was structural. Her main beam broke.

Most of the men on her upper deck at the time (230) were saved. About 70 of the many people below were saved, including eleven women. All sailors used to maintain that among the saved was a little boy who was found clinging to the neck of one of the ship's sheep, that as no-one knew his name, the Navy adopted him, and that he rose to be an Admiral. I hope that some of this may be true. However

> Down went the *Royal George*
> With twice four hundred men.

Some fifty years later, Captain Marryat made bold use of Ingram's story, printing it almost all, with changes much for the worse, as an old seaman's yarn in the story *Poor Jack*.

Divers proved that the wreck was not worth the cost and

trouble of lifting, the hull being old and rotten. In the course of time the wreck was blown up so that it might not foul the anchorage. At the time of her sinking, the ship was about 37 years old. She had been much at sea, had been one of the wonders of her time, the loftiest ship afloat, and far more heavily armed than any ship in the world. Age had caused her rig and armament to be much reduced, at the time of her loss. Many have suggested that she ought to have been broken-up long before her end.

At some time after her sinking, booksellers and publishers issued accounts of her (Ingram's and other records) bound in thin pieces of wood from her wreck. No doubt some of these curiosities may still survive here and there; but I have not seen one lately.

* * *

The *Captain* was an early experimental steam turret ship designed by Captain Cowper Coles in the late 1860's. She was one of the results of the then new theory that the days of broadside fire were over, and that war ships should have low free-board, and a few heavy guns in revolving turrets. It is said that some errors and misunderstandings gave her less stability than her designer had planned. She had small bunker capacity. Her masts were of a new tripod design which added much to her danger.

In 1870 she went out to cruise with the Channel Fleet. In stormy worsening weather, the Admiral of the squadron passed an afternoon on board her watching her very carefully. In the evening (it was said) he was pressed to spend the night on board her, but declined, and returned to his flagship. He is said to have said that he was never more thankful to get away from any ship, as the *Captain* had a sinister movement that was new to his

experience. The night came on with darkness and violence. In the midnight hours her lights disappeared: in the
morning she was missing from the squadron. The ships,
turning back upon their course, soon came upon floating
wreckage from her. Later, it was found that a few survivors had landed at a Spanish port. The ship had turned
over and gone down. The survivors had contrived to reach
a boat floating bottom upward, had righted her and made
port in her. Save for these few, all hands were gone. With
one exception (the stories said) the survivors were from
the watch on deck at the time.

The exception (according to the tale) was a gunnery
officer, who woke up suddenly in his cabin, with the
feeling that he must instantly go on deck to look to his
guns. He obeyed the prompting, went instantly on deck,
and at the next instant was in the sea with the ship turning
over and filling.

*   *   *

The *Eurydice* was a sailing training frigate coming home
from a winter cruise in the West Indies with over three
hundred naval lads and boys on board. She made the
Channel in cold blustery March weather (1878) on a
Saturday. Her hands were cracking-on, it is said, so that
they might be in Portsmouth Harbour that night. She was
under all plain sail not far from the southern coast of the
Isle of Wight in what seems to have been violent clearing
North-westerly weather, very fierce in some of the gusts,
especially off the mouth of any gully in the land. She was
making ready to anchor. She had a certain scope of cable
ready ranged on her gun deck on the starboard (the lee)
side. She had some at least of her forward lee ports open.
She was greatly admired as she passed along the island in
all the beauty of a full-rigged ship with the wind a point or

two free blowing fresh, and logging probably a full ten knots.

Coming round the bend, and hauling her wind for Spithead, she had the ill-fate to be over set. A gust of a most unusual tempestuous violence, that scattered destruction among the tiles and chimney-pots of the island towns, swept down upon her and struck her on the beam. As it struck her, she buried her starboard bow, took, instantly, a great volume of water through her open ports, and (as Naval officers supposed) continued her swift passage sailing fast downwards, filling as she went, till she stove in her starboard bow against the bottom.

It had been so sudden a squall that nothing had been let fly: no halliards were let go: the helmsman had no chance to let her go off. The gear was so good that nothing gave. It was said that she was fitted with experimental wire standing-rigging, and that all of it stood.

In the bitterly cold March sea almost all hands were lost with her.

The wreck was later raised, beached, examined and broken-up. The hull had been badly damaged and mud had silted into every crevice everywhere.

Like the *Royal George*, the loss of the *Eurydice* inspired some verses. Those by G. M. Hopkins and Sir A. Conan-Doyle have helped to keep her in public memory: and only a little while ago a lady wrote to tell of the destruction ashore of the gust that sank her.

ON MOONSAILS

Looking out upon the Mersey, day-in, day-out, in the last great days of sailing-ships, one pleasure was to see some very lofty ships, one hope, to see a ship with a moonsail yard. There were then many lofty ships in the world, some that made the heart leap and then stand still; a good many of these crossed skysail yards (sometimes the sixth; in very modern ships, the seventh, yard from the deck) but not any crossed a moonsail yard.

Asking the old seamen about us, whether we should ever see a moonsail yard, the answer was 'No. Only two ships have ever crossed a moonsail yard, the *Lightning*, and the *James Baines*.' Then would follow some tale of the *James Baines*, or of James Baines himself, both then fresh in memory on the Mersey; but now dimmed; and we would return to scan all incoming ships or new arrivals in the docks, for some wonder with a glory-pole on which a seventh or an eighth yard was crossed (according to the arrangement of her topgallants).

Then, on one memorable clear breezy morning, 'with the wind at South-west, boys,' the wonder was there. Somewhere about the Queen's Dock, lay a big, very lofty American ship in splendid order, with single topgallants, and, on her main, at some incredible height, a seventh yard, a sure-enough moonsail yard, the talk of all hands, the long-sought Phoenix, the planet come into ken.

Every glass was turned upon her, every eye feasted on her. We did not care what she was, nor what she brought to us, her moonsail was enough for us.

'And many prayed, who never prayed before' that she might still be there when Leave was given, so that they might lay out upon that wonder, and thereafter boast, perhaps two generations later. 'I know the old . . . and laid out upon her moonsail yard. Ships were ships in those days, etc.' This joy was not granted to us. As suddenly as she had come, the wonder vanished, and came not again. We judged that she had been plucked away to discharge, or to load, elsewhere. What she was and what became of her, we never knew: only that she was a big American full-rigged ship, exceedingly lofty, very heavily sparred, in splendid order, and crossing a main moonsail.

In later years, in talking with sailors, I have heard suggestions as to the ship. I have not verified these. At the time, we could with little trouble have learned the name and details, but in youth fresh interests follow swiftly, and now even the date of her appearance has telescoped itself into the past, as a very long time ago.

During that time, cynics have sometimes said, 'Are you sure, that it was a moonsail yard?' and when I have said 'Yes,' they have sometimes answered, 'A good many seamen went to some lengths to make their ships look smart. Navy men would ship show-poles above their royal masts. American captains had always a wonderful supply of spars; and no men have ever taken greater pride in their ships. What you saw was perhaps not a real moonsail yard, but something that looked like one for the occasion of coming into port. It may have been some quite light fake, made of bamboo, or very light wood, with a faked sail furled on it, and needing only the lightest of lifts and braces. It would have looked superb, and the look was all that was sought: a boy of 12 could have sent it up and down, and the sail would never have been set.'

All this is possible and even likely, but even so, to us boys who saw and admired, the thing was a moonsail yard, and we tell the truth when we say that we have seen one.

Many years later, an old sailor told me that when he was in the old . . . (name long since forgotten) they always set moonsails above the three skysails in fair weather, but that these moonsails were small light triangular sails not set upon yards. Just under the trucks there were halliard blocks through which the halliards led abaft the masts down to the bitts on deck. These halliards ran the apex of each triangle up to just below the truck. The moonsails' clues were lashed to the skysail yard-arms. The sails, when furled, were secured with the skysail gaskets, almost as if they were parts of the skysails. When set, perhaps the halliards that hoisted them also hoisted the skysails.

This arrangement made necessary a re-arrangement of the skysail-stay, which ran to just below the truck upon a traveller when the moonsail was set and kept the stay before-all. The stay came down with the sail if necessary.

All these butterfly sails and the light spars upon which they set could be swiftly stowed and struck. Any active boy of 13 or 14 could have furled a moonsail and skysail together; and then, helped by another boy, have sent down the skysail yard and the gunter, or show-pole, or light spar, which it had crowned.

For a few years, in some services, ships were not reckoned much for looks unless they crossed at least one skysail. One of the very last of all big sailing-ships crossed a main skysail yard. I like to think that sometimes in the Trades she ran up a triangular moonsail above it, for old time's sake, and for glory.